Nifast
Manual Handling Instruction

Manual Handling Instruction
FETAC Level 6

Nifast

GILL EDUCATION

Gill Education
Hume Avenue
Park West
Dublin 12
www.gilleducation.ie

Gill Education is an imprint of M.H. Gill & Co.

© Nifast 2013

978 07171 5730 3

Print origination by Síofra Murphy
Illustrations by Derry Dillon
All images courtesy of Shutterstock and Presenter Media
Printed and bound by CPI Group (UK) Ltd, Croydon, CR0 4YY

A CIP catalogue record for this book is available from the British Library.

Contents

Chapter 3 Ergonomic Principles and Risk Assessment

Chapter 4 Manual Handling Principles and Techniques

Chapter 5 Planning and Design of Manual Handling Training Programmes

Chapter 6 Delivery of Manual Handling Training

Chapter 1

Legislative Requirements and Health Benefit

Chapter Outline

- Explain the main component of relevant health and safety legislation and guidance documents to include the current Manual Handling of Loads Regulations, and principles of prevention as outlined in the current Safety, Health and Welfare at Work Act and relevant guidance from government and professional bodies.

- Evaluate the health and organisational benefits of an integrated approach to the management of manual handling to include development of a manual handling policy, staff consultation, risk assessment, implementation of appropriate controls and relevant training.

Health and Safety

Health and safety is:

- A condition free from risk of injury or threat to health and wellbeing.

- An objective to be achieved; it is not a natural state of affairs.

The cost of accidents to Irish society as a whole is €3.6 billion each year. Lower back pain affects approximately 80 per cent of the population at some stage in life. Healthcare costs and the cost of sick leave and early retirement because of back pain are estimated at €800 million. On average, 7,000 non-fatal work injuries are reported each year to the Health and Safety Authority (HSA), 27 per cent of which account for handling, lifting or carrying loads.

There is a financial cost associated with all accidents, including hidden costs, which can be broken into:

1. *Insured costs*: Injury, illness and damage.

2. *Uninsured costs*: Product and material damage; plant and building damage; tool and equipment damage; legal costs; expenditure on emergency supplies; cost of clearing site; production delays; overtime and temporary labour; investigation time; supervisor's time diverted; clerical effort; fines; and loss of experience/expertise.

Safety, Health and Welfare at Work Act 2005

Legislation provides minimum standards to protect the safety and health of workers, and the main legal framework for this is set out in the Safety, Health and Welfare at Work Act 2005. The 2005 Act places specific duties on both employers and employees and these duties are general to any aspect of safety, health and welfare within the workplace.

An overview of the Act includes the following elements:

1. General duties, comparable to those in compensation claims, are imposed on all people in all places of work, public and private sector, in connection with safety, health and welfare. This includes employers, employees, the self-employed, manufacturers, designers and builders. The difference between the duties in the 2005 Act and those applicable in compensation claims is that failure to comply with the duties in the 2005 Act may lead to a criminal prosecution.

2. In order to comply with their duties, these duty holders must do what is 'reasonably practicable', which is defined for the first time in the 2005 Act.

3. An employer must ensure that its activities are managed in a way that prevents accidents or ill health; or, for example, improper conduct or behaviour (which covers stress and bullying). An employer must train employees where a risk assessment states that such training is required. Competent persons must be appointed to ensure the implementation of these duties.

4. Employees must take reasonable care of their own safety and that of others; must not engage in improper conduct or behaviour; must attend training required by a risk assessment;

and must not be under the influence of 'an intoxicant', defined as drugs and alcohol.

5. All organisations, public and private sector, must compile a Safety Statement, based on prior hazard identification and risk assessment, setting out how safety, health and welfare is being 'managed and secured' and also the protective and preventative strategies to control risks.

6. Failure to comply with the general duties in the 2005 Act carries the potential of a fine of up to €5,000 and/or a prison term of up to 12 months even on conviction in the District Court, with up to 2 years' imprisonment and/or a maximum fine of up to €3 million on conviction on indictment.

7. Provision for fixed charge offences ('on-the-spot fines') with penalties up to €1,000 are also included in the 2005 Act.

8. The Health and Safety Authority is the regulatory body for the 2005 Act, and is empowered to promote awareness of safety and health at work and to enforce the law by means of enforcement notices and prosecutions where necessary.

The duties contained in the 2005 Act are subject to the limitation that employers and others are required to do only what is **reasonably practicable**. This is very similar to the 'reasonable' duty of care that applies in compensation claims. Section 2(6) of the 2005 Act sets out the first statutory definition of what is reasonably practicable.

The essential elements of this legal standard are that an employer:

- Has exercised all due care.

- Has put in place necessary protective and preventative measures.

- Has identified hazards and assessed risks likely to result in accidents or ill health.

- Is not required to take further measures where these would be grossly disproportionate having regard to the unusual, unforeseeable and exceptional nature of the circumstances.

This definition provides a useful basis for deciding what is required by the general duties in the 2005 Act, and in any specific regulations that also use the phrase.

Part II Section 8 – Duties of Employers

The 2005 Act outlines both general and specific duties of employers to employees. The **general duty of care** outlines that 'it shall be the duty of every employer to ensure, so far as is reasonably practicable, the safety, health and welfare at work of their employees'. **Specific duties of employers** include the following:

- Managing work activities to ensure the safety, health and welfare of their employees.

- Managing work activities to prevent any improper conduct/behaviour which is likely to put the health and safety of employers at risk.

- Provision of a safe place of work.

- Provision of safe access and egress.

- Provision of safe plant, machinery and other articles and substances.

- Provision of a safe system of work.

- Maintaining adequate welfare facilities.

- Provision of information, instruction, training and supervision.

- Implementing necessary protective and preventative measures.

- Having regard to the general principles of prevention in schedule 3.

- Preparation of adequate emergency plans.

- Reporting prescribed accidents and dangerous occurrences.

- Obtaining the services of a competent person to ensure the safety, health and welfare at work of employees.

Section 10 of the 2005 Act refers to health and safety training in general. In summary, health and safety training should:

- Be provided without any loss of remuneration for employees.

- Be adapted to take account of new or changed risks.

- Be provided as required, on commencement of employment or on change of tasks.

- Be appropriate to the tasks and provided by a competent person.

- Provide appropriate information with respect to the health and safety risks.

- Be provided as appropriate for both fixed-term employees and temporary employees.

Part III, section 22 of the 2005 Act relates to health surveillance. It implies that employers should take into consideration the physical capabilities of employees with respect to manual handling activities. Schedule 3 of the Safety, Health and Welfare at Work (General Application) Regulations 2007 (regulation 69) states that 'the employee may be at risk if he or she is physically unsuited to carry out the task in question'.

Part II Section 13 – Duties of Employees

Part II, section 13 of the 2005 Act also places duties on employees in the workplace; an employee shall:

- Comply with the relevant statutory provisions and take reasonable care for their safety and that of others.

- Not be under the influence of an 'intoxicant' so as to endanger their safety and that of others.

- Submit to any appropriate, reasonable and proportionate tests for intoxicants.

- Co-operate with an employer in order to comply with relevant statutory provisions.

- Not engage in improper conduct which is likely to endanger their safety or that of others.

- Attend training and take into account training and instruction.

- Make correct use of any article/substance provided, including the use of suitable personal protective clothing and equipment (PPCE).

- Report known defects.

General Application Regulations 2007 – Manual Handling of Loads

The General Application Regulations 2007 are implemented under the Safety, Health and Welfare at Work Act 2005 and they contain detailed legal requirements on fifteen areas of health and safety. The specific regulations applying directly to manual handling are General Provisions Regulations and Manual Handling of Loads Regulations (part II, chapter 4, and schedule 3).

Regulation 68 – Definition of Manual Handling

Regulation 68 of the 2007 Regulations provides a wide definition of the term 'manual handling of loads':

> … any transporting or supporting of a load by one or more employees and includes lifting, putting down, pushing, pulling, carrying, or moving a load, which, by reason of its characteristics or of unfavourable ergonomic conditions, involves risk, particularly of back injury, to employees.

The equivalent British Manual Handling Operations Regulations 1992 specify that 'load' include a human or animal. The Irish 2007 Regulations do not mention animals or humans; however, it can be assumed that they are implied in the legislation.

Regulation 69 – Duties of Employers

Regulation 69 of the 2007 Regulations outlines that an employer shall:

- Take appropriate organisational measures or use the appropriate means, in particular mechanical equipment, to avoid the need for the manual handling of loads by the employer's employees.

- Where the need for the manual handling of loads by the employer's employees cannot be avoided, take appropriate organisational measures, use appropriate means or provide the employer's employees with such means in order to reduce the risk involved in the manual handling of such loads, having regard to the factors specified in schedule 3.

- Wherever the need for manual handling of loads by the employer's employees cannot be avoided, organise workstations in such a way as to make such handling as safe and healthy as possible, and:

  - Taking account of the risk factors for the manual handling of loads specified in schedule 3, assess the health and safety conditions of the type of work involved and take appropriate measures to avoid or reduce the risk, particularly of back injury, to the employer's employees;

  - Ensure that particularly sensitive risk groups of employees are protected against any dangers which specifically affect them in relation to the manual handling of loads and the individual risk factors, having regard to the risk factors set out in schedule 3;

  - Ensure that where tasks are entrusted to an employee, their capabilities in relation to safety and health are taken into account, including, in relation to the manual handling of loads by employees, the individual risk factors set out in schedule 3;

  - When carrying out health surveillance in relation to the manual handling of loads by employees, take account of the appropriate risk factors set out in schedule 3;

- Without prejudice to section 9 of the 2005 Act, ensure that those of the employer's employees who are involved in manual handling of loads receive general indications and, where possible, precise information on the weight of each load and the centre of gravity of the heaviest side when a package is eccentrically loaded.

Risk Assessment where Manual Handling Is Unavoidable

Regulation 69(b) of the 2007 Regulations states that where the need for manual handling cannot be avoided, the employer must, in order to reduce the risk involved in the manual handling of loads:

● Use appropriate means to reduce the risk.

● Take appropriate organisational measures to reduce the risk.

● Provide employees with the means to reduce the risk.

Examples of using appropriate means to reduce the risk include automating the process, such as using suction lifts to move heavy boxes, and mechanising the process, such as using a forklift or pallet truck to move equipment. **Note**: The introduction of automation or mechanisation may introduce additional hazards and risks, and such risks must also be assessed.

Examples of organisational measures to reduce the risk include rotating employees from heavy to light work; allowing for the provision of adequate rest breaks to allow recovery from muscular fatigue; allowing for the provision of two employees to carry out heavy tasks; marking or tagging heavy items; and providing appropriate manual handling training.

The HSA *Guide to the Safety, Health and Welfare at Work (General Applications) Regulations 2007* provides the following examples of solutions used to address manual handling in this context:

Issue	Risk Factors	Solution
Operator has to remove product from a caged container.	This requires repetitive bending and over-stretching.	Source a container with a removable side, which allows the operator to reach the bottom without over-stretching, or source a mechanical aid, which allows the container to be raised at an angle thus reducing the bending activity.
Manual handling 60 kg sacks to hoppers.	The load is too heavy. The effort is made with the body in an unstable posture.	Provide scissor lifts with rotating turntables and reduce sack weight to 25 kg.
Nursing staff have to help infirm patients by supporting them to the bathroom and helping them in and out of the bath. The patients are awkward to handle and heavy, presenting a considerable risk of back injury. There is not enough room to use a patient hoist.	Physical effort too strenuous. The physical effort is made with the body in an unstable posture.	After consultation, present proposed changes to the bathroom layout to create more space, by replacing partitions with curtains and moving the bath away from the wall, giving room to use the patient hoist and enabling staff to get to both sides of the bath.

Source: Health and Safety Authority (2007)

Regulation 69(c) of the 2007 Regulations states that the employer must organise workstations in such a way as to make manual handling as safe and healthy as possible, and that the employer must assess the health and safety conditions of the type of work involved having regard to the general reference factors specified in schedule 3 to the 2007 Regulations.

Schedule 3 ✳

Schedule 3 of the Manual Handling of Loads Regulations (regulation 69) outlines five reference or risk factors which should be assessed as part of a manual handling risk assessment. These are the individual risk factors for the development of musculoskeletal problems.

1. Characteristics of the Load

The Regulations state that the manual handling of a load may present a risk, particularly of back injury, if it is: (a) too heavy or too large; (b) unwieldy or difficult to grasp; (c) unstable or has contents likely to shift; (d) positioned in a way requiring it to be held or manipulated at a distance from the trunk, or with a bending or twisting of the trunk; or (e), likely, because of its contours or consistency (or both), to result in injury to employees, particularly in the event of a collision.

Where the above manual handling hazards and an associated risk of musculoskeletal injury is identified, the ergonomic control measures necessary to reduce the risk may be evident from considering the following:

- Can the load be made lighter by being packaged into smaller containers or packages?
- Can the load be made less bulky to allow it to be held closer to the body?
- Can the load be made easier to lift by changing the shape or surface texture?
- Can handles or a sling be provided to move the load?

- Is the load designed or packaged so that the contents will not shift unexpectedly?

ⵣ *2. Physical Effort Required*

The Regulations state that a physical effort may present a risk, particularly of back injury, if it is: (*a*) too strenuous; (*b*) only achieved by a twisting movement of the trunk; (*c*) likely to result in a sudden movement of the load; or (*d*) made with the body in an unstable posture.

Where the physical effort poses a risk of injury, the following are some solutions which can be employed to reduce the associated risk:

- Using mechanical aids e.g. scissor lifts, forklifts and cranes.

- Reducing the weight of the load e.g. specifying the size of packages required to suppliers.

- Providing grips or handles on boxes or other equipment.

- Moving by sliding rather than lifting.

- Using powered conveyors, roller trays or trolleys to move equipment.

- Designing the work area to allow for easy access by mechanical equipment.

- Designing the work area to suit the physical needs of the employee.

✗ *3. Characteristics of the Working Environment*

The Regulations state that the characteristics of the working environment may increase a risk, particularly of back injury, if: (*a*) there is not enough room, in particular vertically, to carry out the activity; (*b*) the floor is uneven or slippery; (*c*) the place of work or the working environment prevents the handling of loads at a safe height or with good posture by the employee; (*d*) there are variations in the level of the floor or the working surface, requiring the load to be manipulated on different levels; (*e*) the floor or foot rest is unstable; or (*f*) the temperature, humidity or ventilation is unsuitable.

✳ 4. Requirements of the Activity

The Regulations state that the activity may present a risk, particularly of back injury, if it entails one or more of the following requirements: (a) over-frequent or over-prolonged physical effort involving in particular the spine; (b) an insufficient bodily rest or recovery period; (c) excessive lifting, lowering or carrying distances; or (d) a rate of work imposed by a process that cannot be altered by the employee.

The following provides some guidance with respect to reducing the physical demands of the activity:

- Consider reducing the frequency of the task if this is a risk factor for musculoskeletal disorder.

- Conserve as much energy as possible by taking frequent rest breaks appropriate to the task, minimising the amount of static muscular effort required.

- Consider reducing the distance over which the load must be carried.

- The fitter and more flexible the employee, the less likelihood there is for development of musculoskeletal injury.

- An increased risk exists when the load is located above shoulder height or below mid-thigh height.

- Where a process is dictating the pace of manual handling in combination with repetitive and continuous movement, the employee is at greater risk of upper limb disorders.

5. Individual Risk Factors

The employee may be at risk if they: (a) are physically unsuited to carry out the task in question; (b) are wearing unsuitable clothing, footwear or other personal effects; or (c) do not have adequate or appropriate knowledge or training.

In determining whether an employee is physically suitable to carry out manual handling safely, pre-employment health surveillance should be carried out. This will assist in identifying if an employee has a pre-existing back or other musculoskeletal problem.

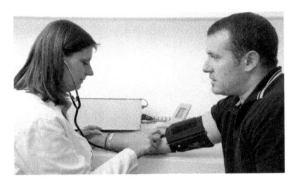

The clothing and footwear worn by employees must not impede safe manual handling, for example tight and restrictive clothing may hinder a person's ability to bend their knees to reach the load at floor level.

Appropriate knowledge and training is addressed in regulation 69(d), which states that the employer must ensure that employees involved in manual handling receive general indications and, where possible, precise information on the weight of each load and the centre of gravity of the heaviest side when a package is eccentrically loaded (lop-sided).

These risk factors, which must be assessed as part of a manual handling assessment, are also known as the TILE mnemonic:

- Requirements of the activity (TASK)

- Physical effort required (INDIVIDUAL)

- Load characteristics (LOAD)

- Characteristics of the working environment (ENVIRONMENT)

Legislation Applicable to Manual Handling

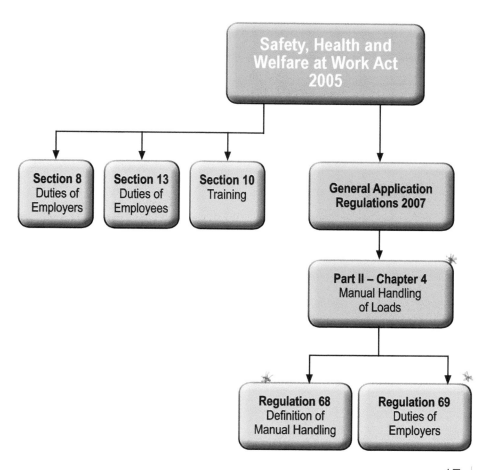

Manual Handling Regulations – Duties of Employers

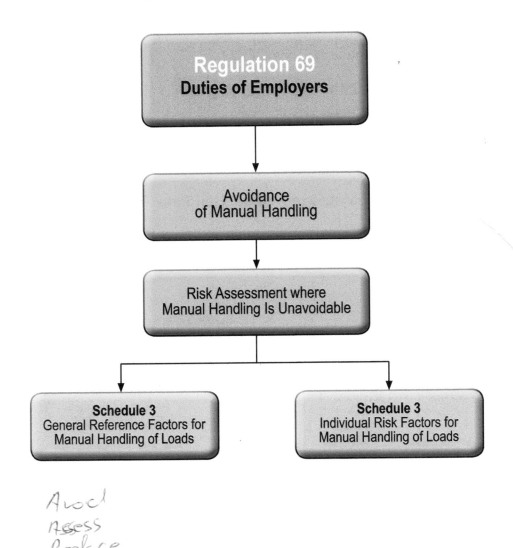

Regulation 69
Duties of Employers

Avoidance
of Manual Handling

Risk Assessment where
Manual Handling Is Unavoidable

Schedule 3
General Reference Factors for
Manual Handling of Loads

Schedule 3
Individual Risk Factors for
Manual Handling of Loads

Avod
Asess
Reduce.
Traing.

Summary of the Risk Assessment Process

STEP 1: Identify the manual handling tasks that need to be assessed

STEP 2: Develop a risk assessment schedule

STEP 3: Carry out the risk assessment process

STEP 3a: Task observation and description
(Gain a detailed understanding of how the task is performed)

STEP 3b: Collect task data
(A well-documented manual handling risk assessment will have good quality information about the task)

STEP 3c: Identify the risk factors
(Schedule 3 details the risk factors for the manual handling of loads – this schedule should be considered in order to identify risk factors in the task)

STEP 3d: Solution development and action plan
(This is the process of eliminating or reducing risk factors)

STEP 4: Review the effectiveness or control measures of the solution

Source: Health and Safety Authority (2007)

Chapter 2

Anatomy and Back Care

Chapter Outline

- Explain the function of the musculoskeletal system.

- Describe the main components of the musculoskeletal system.

- Understand the common occupational back disorders and injury mechanisms.

- Be aware of the importance of posture, fitness and flexibility.

The Musculoskeletal System

The human body's ability to move rests upon the use of muscles and bones which constitute the musculoskeletal system. This system gives the body form and shape, and provides the body with support and stability. It is responsible for bodily movements. The musculoskeletal system is a combination of the muscular and the skeletal components of the human body. The skeleton is the bony framework of the body and the muscular system is made up of soft tissue, which includes muscles and tendons. Other components of the musculoskeletal system, which will be discussed below, are ligaments, cartilage and discs.

The Skeleton

The skeleton has two distinct parts:

1. The axial skeleton (central core) consisting of the skull, rib cage and spinal column (vertebral column).

2. The appendicular skeleton consisting of the limbs (arms and legs), which perform the movements involved in manual handling.

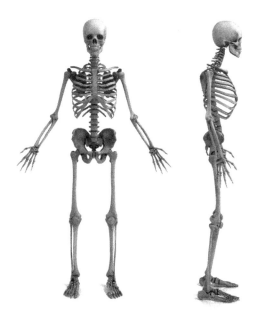

The function of the skeleton is to:

- Provide the body with a defined shape.

- Provide support.

- Facilitate movement of the joints (appendicular skeleton).

- Provide protection of the internal organs.

- Provide structure for the attachment of muscles.

Bones

There are four categories of bones:

Bone Category	Example	Function
Long bones	Long bones of the limbs such as the humerus in the arm and the femur or thigh bone.	Involved in large, robust movements.
Short bones	Bones that make up the fingers and toes.	Finger bones are involved in gripping movements.
Flat bones	Bones such as the skull, shoulder blade (scapula), ribs and pelvis.	Involved in the protection of internal organs.
Irregular bones	Bones of the palm of hand or arch of foot, and vertebrae of the spinal column.	Provide shape to the body.

Joints

Joints are formed by the joining together of two or more bones for the purpose of movement. The bone ends are covered with cartilage and this provides ease of movement. Cartilage is a tough fibrous tissue, which also provides protection.

There are three types of joints:

1. Moveable

2. Partly moveable

3. Fixed.

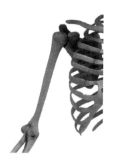

Moveable joints have synovial fluid which lubricates the bone ends, for example knee and shoulder joints, the joints of the upper and lower limbs, and the facet joints of the spine.

Partly moveable joints include the joints between the vertebrae, the small joints of the hands and feet, and where the hip bone and sacrum meet.

Fixed joints (there is no movement) include the skull and sacrum. The bones ends have a fine layer of cartilage.

The Muscular System

Muscles are made of soft elastic tissue, which contract and relax, and are essential for movement. They receive messages to do so from the brain via the nerve supply. Muscles have a rich blood supply.

There are two main types of muscles:

1. *Postural muscles*: These are the small short muscles that form the trunk; they use available oxygen and tire less easily. The abdominal (stomach) muscles have an important postural function and are essential in protecting the back from injury. They act to maintain the lumbar curvature of the lower back.

23

2. *Action or long muscles*: The action muscles are long muscles such as the muscles of the back and limbs. These use stored energy and tire faster. Muscles can lengthen, shorten or remain taut depending on the needs of the body.

Main Muscle Groups of the Body

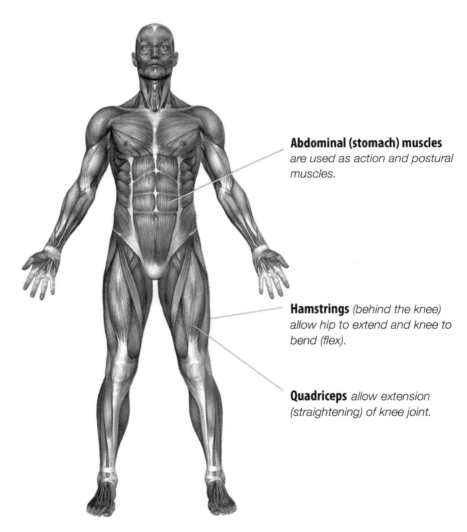

Abdominal (stomach) muscles *are used as action and postural muscles.*

Hamstrings *(behind the knee) allow hip to extend and knee to bend (flex).*

Quadriceps *allow extension (straightening) of knee joint.*

Ligaments

Ligaments are tough non-elastic bands which hold bones together. They consist of fibrous tissue, which allow a normal range of movement to occur at a joint, for example the knee joint, but if forced beyond the limit of its pliability, the ligament will tear. Ligaments heal slowly and they have a poor blood supply.

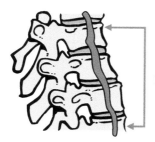

Ligaments *joining the spinal bones (vertebrae) together.*

The ligament on the outside of the ankle is frequently torn during soccer, where a player turns on the ankle, overstretching the ligament fibres and at worst tearing the complete ligament. In some cases, ligaments may take longer than fractures to heal due to the poor blood supply.

Capsule

The capsule is fibrous tissue surrounding the joints like a sleeve. There are capsules surrounding the facet joints of the spine and all other joints such as the knee and shoulder joints. In arthritic conditions, the joint capsule can become inflamed.

Cartilage

Cartilage is found between the bone ends forming a joint. It protects joint surfaces from wear and tear.

Anatomy of the Spine

The human spine is a flexible column of 33 bones called vertebrae.

There are:

- Seven cervical vertebrae (neck).

- Twelve thoracic or dorsal vertebrae (chest area).

- Five lumbar vertebrae (lower back).

- Five sacral vertebrae (fused together forming one bone – the sacrum).

- Four coccygeal vertebrae (forming the coccyx or tail bone).

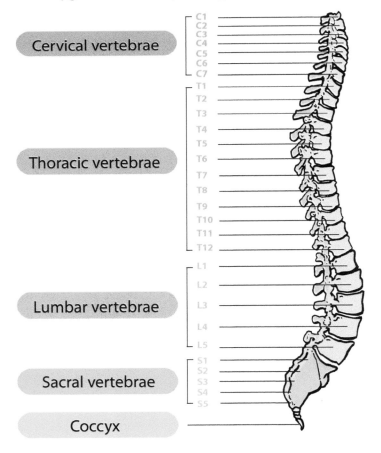

Cervical vertebrae
C1 C2 C3 C4 C5 C6 C7

Thoracic vertebrae
T1 T2 T3 T4 T5 T6 T7 T8 T9 T10 T11 T12

Lumbar vertebrae
L1 L2 L3 L4 L5

Sacral vertebrae
S1 S2 S3 S4 S5

Coccyx

The uppermost vertebrae support the skull, and the sacrum articulates with the pelvic bones. The ribs are attached in pairs to each of the 12 thoracic vertebrae. Between any two vertebrae there is limited movement, but when the spine moves as a unit there is considerable range of movement.

The spinal column has three curves which allow it to bend in a synchronised fashion. There is a concave (inward) curve of the neck area, a convex (outward) curve of the thoracic spine and a concave curvature of the lumbar spine. Observed from the side, the spinal column is S-shaped, and this is the normal posture of the spinal column.

A Typical Vertebra

A typical spinal bone or vertebra has a body and an arch. The body is the curved mass toward the front of the bone, with a cartilage plate on both the top and the bottom of the body. It is surrounded by ligaments, which attach to the bone above

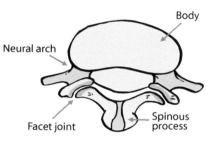

and below. The arch points backward and is attached to the back of the body of the vertebra toward each side. The projections or bumps on the vertebra are for ligament and muscle attachment. It has four articular facets – two upper and two lower – forming joints with adjacent vertebrae.

The vertebral segments are the functional units of the spine and consist of:

- Two vertebrae with their cartilage attachments.

- A spinal disc sandwiched between the vertebrae.

27

- Ligaments surrounding the bones and attaching one vertebra to another.

- Partly moveable joints between the vertebral bodies.

- Moveable facet joints.

Discs

Discs are located between each vertebra and are composed of an outer fibro-cartilaginous ring and an inner pulpy elastic material. The inner material is a pulpy substance known as the 'nucleus'.

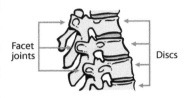

The function of the disc is to:

- Cushion shock.

- Keep the vertebrae apart.

- Allow the spinal nerves to exit freely.

- Allow movement between vertebrae.

The outer annulus of the disc receives a small blood supply from the endplate of the vertebral body, which is facilitated by movement and exercise to provide nutrients and metabolism. Nerves

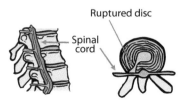

supply a small part of the outer ring of the disc and therefore pain can be felt even if there is slight damage to the disc.

Discs are composed mostly of water but then dry out with age. The process of desiccation is hardly noticeable until around the age of 30, when the outer fibres begin to degenerate and crack. The pulpy nucleus dries out gradually, resulting in much thinner discs by the age of about 60. Although disc protrusions are unusual by this age, thin discs can cause problems, particularly for the facet joints. A disc protrusion (lesion or slipped disc) involves a rupture

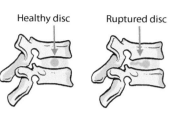

Healthy disc   Ruptured disc

of the outer rings, allowing the nucleus to move out and backward, causing a pressure on the spinal nerve.

Muscles of the Spine

The spine depends on muscles for stability. They control the position of the spine and the trunk, and provide movement and power for voluntary activity.

The main muscles controlling the spine are:

1. *The extensor muscles*: These run between the vertebrae, and allow flexion, extension and side bending of the spine. They are long thin muscles.

2. *The abdominal muscles*: The abdominal muscles have a role in supporting the lumbar spine. The transverse fibres of the abdominal muscles act as postural muscles in stabilising the lower back area. If the transverse muscle group is weak, the lower back may fall into a 'sway back' posture.

Joints of the Spine

The joints of the spine consist of the:

1. Facet joints (synovial joints).

2. Secondary cartilaginous joints (between disc and intervertebral bodies).

Both the facet joints and the secondary cartilaginous joints form a functional unit and any alternation in the thickness of the disc or in its elasticity interferes with the smooth movement of these joints. Between the bodies of the vertebrae, there is a layer of articular cartilage, and when this is damaged, the smooth movement is interfered with and scarring occurs. When scarring occurs, the cartilage is no longer permeable and this can lead to disc degeneration.

Posture, Biomechanics and Back Injury

Back pain is not usually the result of a one-off incident or injury. Many back injuries are the result of a cumulative effect of months or years of having poor posture; incorrect biomechanics; loss of flexibility, strength and general physical fitness; and poor workplace ergonomics. In order to better understand the mechanisms of occupational back injury, it is essential to have a basic understanding of posture and biomechanics.

Posture

Good posture is a good habit which contributes to the wellbeing of an individual. The structure and function of the body provide the potential for attaining and maintaining a good posture. Good posture is a state of muscular and skeletal balance, which protects the supporting structures of the body against injury or deformity. A good posture will allow the muscles to function efficiently.

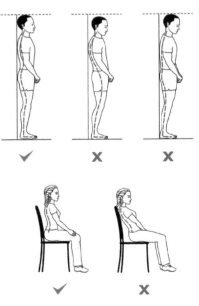

Poor posture is acquired through bad habit and when continued it can contribute to discomfort, stiffness and pain. Poor posture is a faulty relationship between the parts of the body, resulting in increased strain and reduced muscle balance between muscle groups.

Remember: Good posture is a must. 'It is not the load that wears us down, it is the way we carry it.'

A comfortable and well-designed workplace will encourage good working postures. However, even the best-designed office chairs or workstations will not make us sit or stand correctly. When sitting or standing for a long period of time in the same position, muscles will fatigue, resulting in the body changing posture to become more comfortable. There is no one correct sitting or standing posture. Therefore, it is essential to move frequently into different postures, while at the same time maintaining a good alignment of the spine. Frequent changing of position will also promote circulation throughout the body and movement of nutrition into the intervertebral discs.

Remember: 'Our best posture is our next posture.'

Good spinal posture requires adequate muscle strength of the stomach (abdominal) and back muscles, and a balance in strength between both opposing muscle groups. If there is imbalance between both muscle groups, the pelvis will tilt forward or backward resulting in either a 'sway back' or a 'flat back'. Either posture may result in reduced flexibility of the muscles, stiffness and pain.

A good posture of the lower back is maintaining the lower back in a neutral position mid-way between the sway and flat back posture (see below). This neutral position is required when sitting, standing or participating in sport. Regular exercise, which includes flexibility and strengthening exercises, effective body biomechanics, and good working and living postural habits contribute to a healthy spine and significantly reduce the potential for back injury.

Best Postures

Look at the three figures below for a moment and decide which ones are considered best posture and most common poor posture.

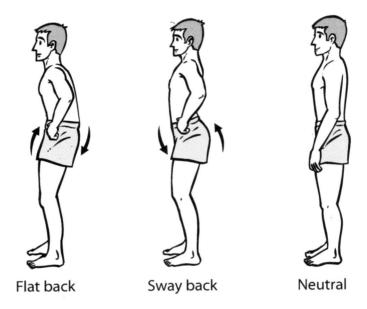

| Flat back | Sway back | Neutral |

The third figure is the best standing posture the human being can achieve in the upright position. Because of the body's structure it cannot stand upright with a straight spine, so the best to hope for is that the trunk and limbs are in good alignment and sufficiently well balanced to cause the minimum of energy expenditure. The line of gravity should lie within the body.

Note: The rule of thumb is ear over shoulder over hip, knee and ankle.

The first figure shows the most common posture fault i.e. the hips are to the fore. If an imaginary line is drawn downward from the hip, it will touch the fore foot or instep instead of the ankle. The resulting tightness will be in the hamstring muscles and upper lumbar spine. The chin usually pokes forward in compensation, thus increasing the neck curve.

To test adequate hamstring length for safe handling practices, ask the subject to sit on the floor with legs straight out in front and knees straight. In the best position the hipbone is directly above the hip joint. The most common fault is that the hipbone is above but behind the hip joint, causing the spine to hump in an effort to keep sitting. The hump is usually most exaggerated in the upper back, suggesting that the upper segments of the lumbar spine are also restricted.

Biomechanics

Biomechanics is the study of how the joints of the body work, with respect to the dynamic and static forces acting on the joints. If the forces and stresses are too high, injuries can occur. Occupational biomechanics explains the mechanics of normal body movement and the mechanisms of injury. The aim of occupational biomechanics is to reduce the incidence of mechanical trauma in the workplace.

Two different types of injury mechanisms are common in industry:

1. Sudden force ➔ impact trauma ➔ lacerations and fractures

2. Repetitive force ➔ overuse trauma ➔ tendonitis, tenosynovitis, back pain etc.

The existence of one or a combination of both of these forces is the leading cause of worker disability in industry.

Mechanics of Movement in the Moveable Spine*

Cervical Spine (Neck)	Thoracic Spine (Between Shoulder Blades and Upper Back)	Lumbar Spine (Lower Back)
Forward and backward bending	Forward and backward bending	Forward – very little
Side to side bending	Side to side bending	Backward – extensive
Rotation (twisting)	Rotation (twisting), which is greatest in this part of the spine (120°)	Side bending – extensive
		Rotation – virtually nil

* The facet (synovial) joints are those that indicate the normal movement of the moveable spine.

Common Occupational Back Disorders and Injury Mechanisms

Soft Tissue Injuries

When the body lacks flexibility in the soft tissues, i.e. muscles, tendons, joint capsules and ligaments, the joints can be damaged by relatively low forces. A structure that does not usually move through its potential full range will become tight, inflexible and easily injured. High forces, such as heavy weights, may also damage flexible joints. If normal joint range is maintained and high forces are avoided, the risk of spinal injury is minimised.

Postural Sprains or Strains

An office worker who sits at a poorly designed workstation or a lorry driver who sits in a slumped posture, without taking adequate breaks, may develop postural stiffness, resulting in postural aches and pains. Over time a combination of spinal stiffness, inflexibility and excessive compression of the discs can lead to disc damage and eventually a disc prolapse. In manual handling tasks, muscular strains can result from the overuse of the spinal muscle groups, lower back inflexibility and excessive forward bending.

Muscle Spasm/Pain

When the body feels pain, its first reaction is to guard the injured part. The muscles in the area will act as a 'splint', and if the pain is prolonged, the guarding may lead to muscle spasm, which is painful. If the pain results from a muscle strain, it is not a serious problem and can be resolved quickly. However, if the pain is the result of an underlying disc lesion or a joint problem, recovery will take longer.

Disc Prolapse/Rupture

Intervertebral discs are made from rings of fibro-cartilage called the annulus fibrosus. These rings surround a central 'jelly-like' substance called the nucleus. This nucleus, however, becomes firmer as the person gets older.

If the disc is compressed, for example when carrying a load, the nucleus is flattened. A combination of the above with bending forward or side bending may result in the nucleus becoming forced through the bands of the annulus, causing a prolapse or rupture of the disc. This is what is commonly referred to as a slipped disc (because of the design of the disc), and it usually occurs at the back and side of the disc.

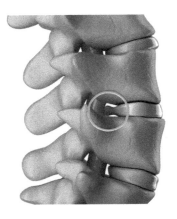

Lumbar disc lesions will present in a number of different ways, such as pain in the area, numbness and weakness, leg pain, and reflex changes in the leg. Effective treatment is a combination of early physiotherapy, strengthening and stretching exercises, and a change in faulty working/living habits. Severe cases may require surgery, which can be very successful.

Bony Injuries

Bony injuries are injuries to the facet joints of the spine. The facet joints stabilise the spine and limit rotation. By its design, the facet joint is subject to compression and shearing forces. If the discs are narrowed through injury or arthritis, changes in the compression forces rise from 25 per cent (healthy spine) to 70 per cent.

Bony injuries can be caused by arthritic changes in the facet joints; fracture of the arch of the vertebrae; fracture of the endplate of the vertebral body leading to disc degeneration; and repetitive extension (backward bending) movements of the spine, for example reaching upward for heavy loads.

Osteoarthritis

Arthritis is a condition that causes an inflammatory response around a joint. This is caused by the facet joints being put into a position of compression when they are not structured to bear weight. This may be due to a reduced disc space, combined with poor spinal postures – usually 'sway back'. The tips of the facets become worn, resulting in a wearing out and roughening of the joint surfaces, leading to pain.

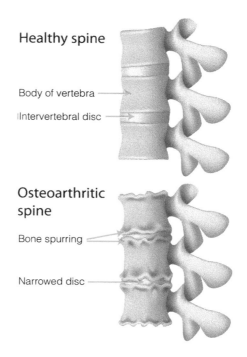

Healthy spine

Body of vertebra

Intervertebral disc

Osteoarthritic spine

Bone spurring

Narrowed disc

37

Habitual poor posture, especially in standing, is sufficient to damage these joints over a period of time. Arthritis may not necessarily cause back pain; research shows that half the population experience changes in the spine as early as 35 years of age. Suitable fitness and flexibility exercises will help to reduce the symptoms of arthritis.

Fractures of the Vertebrae

Fractures can occur in the vertebral bodies as follows: in the front of the bodies in extreme forward bending, and in the endplates i.e. the body of the vertebrae close to and including the cartilage on which the disc rests. This can happen with the spine under load in the erect position or with the curves exaggerated. The end result is that bone repairs with bone and resumes its normal function, but the cartilage heals with scar tissue. This causes diminished nutrition to the discs, which in turn causes disc degeneration.

Sudden Peak Loading

This can occur, for example, when pulling a bed, wheelchair or pallet truck, by using the back instead of the legs, which can cause fracture of the arch. Sudden backward movement under load will not fracture a facet joint because the line of the joint is in line with the movement, but it will force the facet of the bone above down on the arch of the bone below, causing a fracture.

Movement that May Result in Injury to the Spine during Manual Handling

Movement Type	Injury Type
Backward bending (extension of lumbar spine) e.g. pulling backward, lifting down from overhead	Facet joint injury
Forward bending e.g. lifting with back flexed	Muscular or disc injury
Forward bending combined with side bending	Disc prolapse on opposite side
Rotation (twisting of thoracic spine) without moving feet	Sacroiliac joint or thoracic spine injury

The Physiology of Work

Physiology is defined as the science of the chemical processes of life. The relevance of the knowledge of these processes in relation to work can assist in enabling a person to achieve the maximum performance from their musculoskeletal system.

Movement is enabled by muscle activity. Muscle activity needs oxygen and a source of energy to function. Both of these are taken into the body by breathing and eating to be converted into mechanical

energy and heat in the body. This process is called metabolism. The metabolic rate of each individual will affect this process and the rate varies with age, sex, body build etc. If too much fuel in the form of food is taken in, fat may be laid down in the body.

Dietary carbohydrate is stored in the body as glycogen. Glycogen is built from units of glucose. Glucose may be broken down into energy by two processes:

1. *Aerobic system*: This system requires oxygen and sustained activity. Aerobic activity is limited by the availability of oxygen to the working muscle i.e. local blood flow, cardiac output and respiratory function.

2. *Anaerobic system*: This system classifies brief activity, where there is an accumulation of lactate and muscle soreness.

Aerobic and anaerobic systems are complementary. At the beginning of exercise, anaerobic always predominates until the cardiorespiratory system adapts to a new level of demand.

The muscle works by contracting its fibres. Muscle actions may be static or dynamic. In **static activity**, muscles remain the same length to prevent movement or to support loads. In **dynamic activity**, muscles change length and move loads. As the muscle contracts, the pressure within it rises, generating a resistance to blood flow.

In dynamic work with alternate phases of contraction and relaxation, the interruption of blood flow is of short duration. In static work, the blood flow is diminished; the blood supply is unable to meet the demands of work; and there is an accumulation of waste products, such as lactate and heat. In practical terms, this means that static work imposes a greater strain on the heart than dynamic work.

Muscle Strength

A person's strength is defined as the greatest force a person is able to exert in a given situation. Strong muscles are those that bring as many fibres as possible into play. Muscle strength diminishes with age: maximum strength is reached between the ages of 20 and 25, remains more or less constant until about 40 and declines to about 80 per cent of its maximum by about age 65. On average, women are considered to be approximately two-thirds as strong as men and this should be considered when performing manual handling risk assessments.

Muscle Fatigue and Dysfunction

Muscle fatigue is normal and rapidly reversed by rest. Post-exercise soreness follows unaccustomed activity. Symptoms usually peak on the second day after this and disappear within

41

4 to 6 days. The pain is due to the release of histamine and inflammatory substances causing swelling.

Muscle Cramps

The cause of a muscle cramp is mostly unknown and may be from disturbed electrolyte balance or fatigue. It may be triggered by the muscle being in a shortened position, for example the sole of the foot shortened by the weight of bedclothes during sleep.

In conclusion, muscles need energy to work, which is taken in as food and oxygen and converted by the metabolic process. Workers should be encouraged to eat breakfast so as to gain a good level of nutrients early in the day, when work-related injuries commonly occur. (Carbohydrates are a good source of nutrients.) Rest between shifts will alleviate muscle fatigue. Overall, a healthy cardiovascular system will achieve the best results and minimise the likelihood of musculoskeletal damage during prolonged activity.

Prevention of Back Injury

Leading a well-balanced healthy lifestyle is the most effective way to avoid musculoskeletal disorder. Below are a number of health tips.

Exercise programmes: Fitness and exercise programmes should include a cardiovascular element, which can train the heart to pump blood efficiently and without effort. Fitness programmes should also incorporate flexibility, strength and endurance components. If there

is uncertainty about a fitness programme, seek advice from a physiotherapist, medical practitioner or fitness advisor.

Healthy diet: Excess weight can place increased pressure on the joints of the spine and can also contribute to poor posture, thereby causing back problems. A healthy diet is essential for good health.

Good working postures: Achieving good posture will take time and practice. As stated previously, a suitable level of general fitness, including strength and flexibility, will promote good posture. Good working postures will also contribute to improved biomechanics. However, if a person is experiencing an on-going problem with their back, it is essential to seek medical advice.

Management of stress: Stress can cause pain or exacerbate existing pain. A person who is experiencing stress on an on-going basis may tend to adopt poor working postures, resulting in increased exposure to injury. It may also affect the circulation of blood to the muscles, resulting in muscular pain.

Adequate rest: Research shows that adequate regular rest is very beneficial for a person's overall health. If a worker does not take adequate rest, the body will have inadequate time to recover and this will predispose the worker to a greater risk of injury.

Fitness

The well-trained or fit individual will have a broad margin of safety between their maximal power and capacity on the one hand and what is being demanded of them physically on the other. As the work becomes physically less demanding, then some physical activity should be included to provide the stimulus that the body needs to function at its best. The less the body does, the less it is able to do, and the vicious cycle progresses in a downward spiral.

There are four elements to fitness:

1. *Cardiovascular or oxygen transporting system*: If, for example, the particular job at hand requires the heart to pump 10 litres of blood per minute at a rate of 120 beats per minute, it is a definite advantage if the heart is trained to pump 15 litres of blood per minute at a rate of 150 beats per minute.

2. *Strength*: Muscle strength means that more of the muscle fibres (each muscle has between 100,000 and 1,000,000 fibres) are primed to work. It is achieved by high loading/low repetition exercise.

3. *Muscle endurance*: This too depends upon the number of fibres primed to work, but it is also dependent upon the efficiency of the chemical turnover produced by muscle contraction. Muscle fibres work in a relay system i.e. when the energy of some fibres is spent, others take over and the cycle is repeated. Endurance is achieved by low loading/high repetition exercise.

4. *Flexibility*: Flexibility would seem to be the Cinderella of fitness. Little attention is paid to it but it is as important as each of the other three elements. In the usual physical training programme it is either forgotten altogether or such scant attention is paid

to it that the effects are negligible. Flexibility is of particular importance in achieving safe manual handling skills.

Why Flexibility?

The human frame is structured to perform in a certain way. Technology and modern lifestyle mitigate the human body's efficient performance. Without using the body's potential range of movement in the joints and soft tissue structures, they become tight and shortened, thus reducing actual mobility. Muscles lose their elasticity and consequently their range. Tendons, ligaments and connective tissues, because of their fibrous nature, become shortened and stiffness results. The body loses much of the range of movement its brain presumes it has.

Tightened, untreated muscles and soft tissues change the way the body moves. Joints accommodate change and then can become damaged by weight-bearing being inappropriately placed. General circulation can become impaired, and aches and pains are experienced even at rest.

Tightness can be caused by lack of activity; habitual poor posture; poorly co-ordinated movements; favouring the use of one side of the body; un-rehabilitated injury; and pain. This process is often sparked off in young people while studying for exams. If physical activity is neglected and the body is not taken through its full range, it works within its limitations and tightness becomes established. The areas affected are invariably hip and thigh muscles, small of the back, neck, and shoulder girdle.

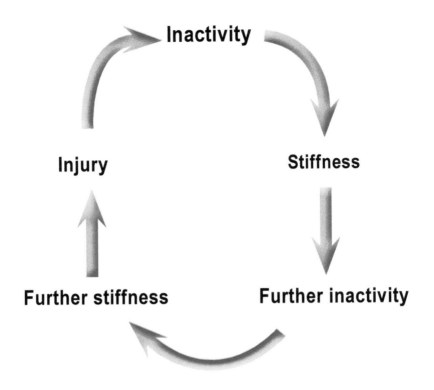

Why Stretch?

Stretching is vital in order to be able to get into a safe position for handling; to allow joint structures (muscles and soft tissues) to function in the best range; to develop body awareness; to prepare the body for activity; and to prevent injury. Everyone, regardless of age or flexibility, can learn to stretch. Flexibility is an extremely important element of fitness, and whether an individual is a top class athlete or sitting at a desk all day, the need to stretch and the technique for stretching remain the same for both.

Stretching can be done at any time but should be done especially before activity. An intensive programme of stretching exercises is

necessary for most people to get them to a safe base position. A healthy lifestyle and good handling skills will maintain an adequate range of flexibility. A good habit is to stretch one or other key area daily.

Remember: Flexibility should be a way of life and not a chore.

How to Stretch

It is important to know what structure is being stretched, for example where does it come from and go to? If it is a muscle, what joint(s) does it pass over? The real function of a muscle or group of muscles must be taken into account. Muscles are stretched so that they are lengthened to the normal range of mobility. A sudden jerking movement into pain is not only ineffective but may seriously damage tissue.

When stretching, take up a safe position where tension is felt and hold for ten seconds. Only go to the point of mild tension. As this is held, the tension should subside. If it does not, ease back slightly to find a position where tension is comfortable.

Easy	A Stretch Developmental	Drastic

This phase (easy stretch) readies the tissues for the developmental stretch, which is what increases flexibility. Then move slowly, smoothly and firmly into a further stretch position and hold for ten seconds. This is the real and effective stretch. The whole exercise must be controlled; do not bounce or jerk (drastic stretch). Breathing should be slow, rhythmical and controlled.

Note: Most people are conditioned to the idea of 'no pain, no gain' and are taught 'the more it hurts, the more you get out of it'. This is not the case. Stretching when done correctly is not painful.

Flexibility Exercises

Lower Lumber Spine

Step 1: Starting position – lying on the floor with both knees bent.

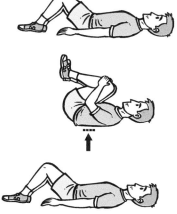

Step 2: Bring both knees up toward the chest as far as possible. Then immediately pull on the knees below the knee joint with the hands.

Step 3: When tension is felt, hold for 10 seconds. Then pull a little further and hold for 10 seconds.

Step 4: Return to starting position. Repeat exercise 5 to 10 times.

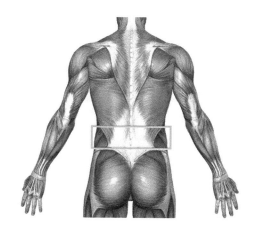

Upper Lumbar Spine

Step 1: Starting position – lying on the floor with both knees bent.

Step 2: Bring both knees up toward the chest as far as possible. Then immediately pull on the knees below the knee joint with both hands.

Step 3: Raise head and shoulders toward knees. When tension is felt, hold for 10 seconds. Then pull a little further and hold for 10 seconds.

Step 4: Return head to starting position **while holding the knees**.

Step 5: Return knees to starting position. Repeat exercise 5 to 10 times.

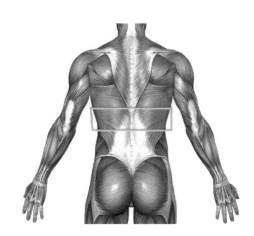

Ileo-psoas and Quadriceps

Step 1: Starting position – kneeling on the floor and sitting back on the heels. Place the hands on the floor underneath the shoulders.

Step 2: Thrust hips forward, raising seat from heels and hold for 10 seconds. When tension is felt, thrust hips a little further forward and hold for 10 seconds.

Step 3: Return to starting position. Repeat exercise 5 to 10 times.

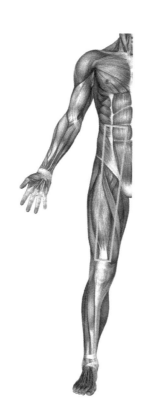

Trunk Rotators

Step 1: Starting position – sitting on the floor with one leg crossed over the other, foot by knee.

Step 2: Turn to side of bent knee and aim to get shoulders approximately 90 degrees to knees. Hold for 10 seconds. When tension is felt, pull a little further and hold for 10 seconds.

Step 3: Return to starting position and repeat on opposite side. Do each side 5 to 10 times.

Hamstring (Lower End)

Step 1: Starting position – standing but half sitting with one leg along a bench or table with knee straight. Place hands behind the back and lean trunk forward at hip joint, keeping back straight.

Step 2: When tension is felt behind the knee, hold for 10 seconds. Then move forward at the hip a little further and hold for a further 10 seconds.

Step 3: Return to starting position and repeat with the other leg. Do exercise 5 to 10 times with each leg.

Hamstring (Upper End)

Step 1: Starting position – lying on the floor with both legs straight. Bend one knee onto chest, pulling with the hand placed underneath the knee.

Step 2: Anchor knee toward chest and attempt to straighten knee joint. When tension is felt at the back of the upper thigh, hold for 10 seconds.

Step 3: Straighten the knee a little more and hold for a further 10 seconds.

Step 4: Return to starting position. Repeat with the other leg. Do exercise 5 to 10 times with each leg.

Note: You are only *attempting* to straighten the knee. It is impossible to achieve a fully straightened knee while the upper hamstring is in this position.

Calf Stretches (Upper End)

Step 1: Starting position – standing in front of a bench or table with feet apart and inner borders parallel.

Step 2: Lean body weight forward, keeping heels on floor, and trunk and legs in a straight line. When tension is felt below and behind the knee, hold for 10 seconds. Lean further forward and hold for a further ten seconds.

Step 3: Return to starting position. Repeat exercise 5 to 10 times.

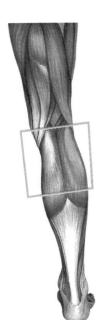

Calf Stretches (Lower End)

Step 1: Starting position – standing with feet apart and inner borders parallel, lean body weight forward by bending the knees and keeping heels on the floor (direct knee over middle toe).

Step 2: When tension is felt above the heel, hold for 10 seconds. Lean further forward and hold for a further 10 seconds.

Step 3: Return to starting position. Repeat this exercise 5 to 10 times.

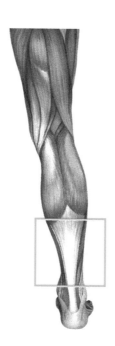

Chapter 3

Ergonomic Principles and Risk Assessment

Chapter Outline

- Describe the concepts of ergonomics to include a description of key ergonomic principles for workplace design, and unfavourable ergonomic conditions, as detailed in the schedule to the current Manual Handling of Loads Regulations.

- Explain the manual handling risk assessment process considering the use of manual handling case studies or scenarios.

- Describe a range of controls to avoid and reduce the risk of injury.

Ergonomics

Ergonomics in the workplace deals with the interaction between people and their equipment and work environment. The ergonomic workplace ensures the health and safety of employees and prevents employee productivity being compromised by poor ergonomic design. The benefits of a workplace ergonomic programme increases comfort, performance, productivity, compliance with health and safety, and employee morale. It reduces the incidence of injury and illness, exposure to insurance claims and insurance costs.

Manual Handling Risk Assessment

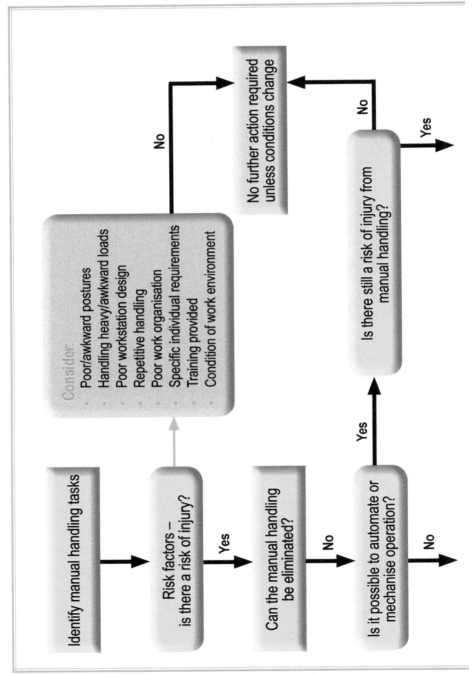

Identify manual handling tasks

Risk factors – is there a risk of injury?

Consider
- Poor/awkward postures
- Handling heavy/awkward loads
- Poor workstation design
- Repetitive handling
- Poor work organisation
- Specific individual requirements
- Training provided
- Condition of work environment

No — No further action required unless conditions change

Yes

Can the manual handling be eliminated?

No

Is it possible to automate or mechanise operation?

No

Yes

Is there still a risk of injury from manual handling?

No — No further action required unless conditions change

Yes

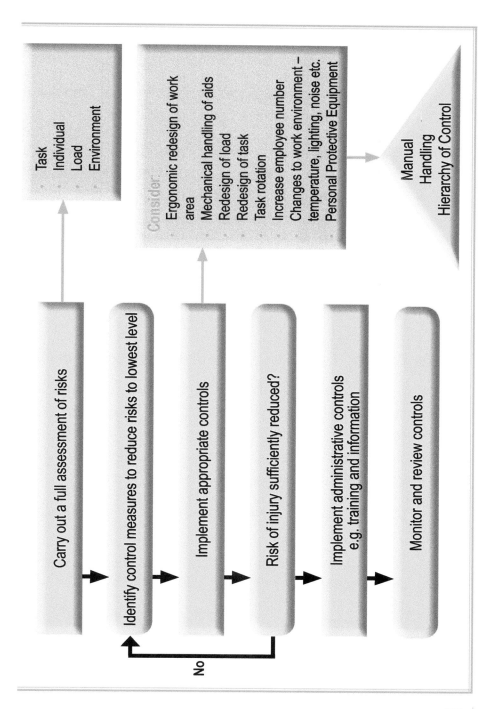

Carry out a full assessment of risks

Task
Individual
Load
Environment

Identify control measures to reduce risks to lowest level

Consider:
Ergonomic redesign of work area
Mechanical handling of aids
Redesign of load
Redesign of task
Task rotation
Increase employee number
Changes to work environment – temperature, lighting, noise etc.
Personal Protective Equipment

Manual Handling Hierarchy of Control

Implement appropriate controls

Risk of injury sufficiently reduced?

No

Implement administrative controls e.g. training and information

Monitor and review controls

The purpose of a manual handling risk assessment is to:

1. Determine if there is a risk of injury to an employee or a number of employees.

2. Implement control measures preferably to eliminate the risk or alternatively to reduce the risk to an acceptable level.

A manual handling risk assessment should focus on the activity in its entirety while identifying and assessing the individual risk factors, outlined as task, individual, load and work environment. Knowledge of the workplace, the system of work and a good understanding of the manual handling activities being carried out are essential when carrying out an effective risk assessment. Confidence in determining whether an activity may be high risk or low risk and in selecting control solutions will be gained with experience.

Tips for Carrying Out a Manual Handling Risk Assessment

When carrying out a manual handling risk assessment, it is beneficial to gather as much information as possible prior to carrying out the assessment, for example information about the work environment, system of work, accident records, previous manual handling risk assessments, number of employees in the area and so on.

1. Consider seeking the assistance of others e.g. engineers and maintenance staff.

2. Determine whether manual handling training has been carried out before – when and what did it cover?

3. Ensure that employees understand what is being done and why.

4. Observe employees carrying out the tasks for an adequate length of time.

5. Discuss the system of work with the supervisor and employees – are the tasks being carried out in accordance with work procedures?

6. Are the principles of safe manual handling being employed? If not, then why not?

7. Ask the supervisor and employees for their advice on solutions, as they are the ones who know the job and may have the ultimate solution.

8. Consider short-term, medium-term and long-term controls – are the controls reasonable?

9. What resources in terms of time, effort and money will be required to implement the controls?

10. Will the workers be willing to comply with the new controls and are they user-friendly?

11. Document the risk assessment results and forward a copy to management.

12. Monitor and review the controls.

An effective method of remembering the hazards to consider when carrying out a manual handling risk assessment is to use the 'TILE' mnemonic:

Task

Individual

Load

Environment

Use this checklist as a reminder when assessing the task. Look at the individual components of the task, bearing in mind the overall system of work, for example time constraints and rest breaks. Has training been provided and did it consider the actual handling tasks being carried out? Does the task require unusual capabilities?

When assessing the individual, observe the working postures of the employee(s). Consider whether the design of the work environment is hindering safe handling practices and good posture. Has any employee a past history of musculoskeletal injury (this information is generally confidential to the HR/occupational health department)?

Postures that can contribute to the development of work-related musculoskeletal disorders (WMSDs) include:

- Excessive bending of the spine.
- Twisting (rotation) and bending of the spine.
- Twisting and backward bending of the spine.
- Working with arms outstretched.
- Working with shoulder girdle elevated (bench height too high).
- Prolonged sitting in a fixed position.

Individual Differences in a Manual Handling/Ergonomic Risk Assessment

When carrying out an ergonomic risk assessment, it is essential to understand that no two individuals have the same levels of strength, flexibility and general fitness. When deciding on workplace design issues to suit individual needs, the following should be considered:

1. *Sex*: The safe load guidelines developed by the British Health Service Executive (HSE) will protect nearly all males and two-thirds of females. Therefore, to protect nearly all females (95 per cent), the guideline figures should be reduced by one-third. The guidelines take into consideration that there are differences in physical strength between most men and women. On average, males are stronger than females by two-thirds.

2. *Age*: The age of the worker can sometimes have an impact on ability to carry out tasks. The risk of manual handling injuries is generally greater for those in their teens or late 50s and 60s. However, it is worth remembering that the experience and knowledge of the older employee can also impact positively.

3. *Pregnancy*: Pregnancy has significant implications for the risk of manual handling injury. Hormonal changes can affect ligaments, increasing the potential for injury. Postural problems can also increase as the pregnancy progresses. Employers must also bear in mind that women involved in manual handling are at risk of injury in the first three months following childbirth.

4. *General health status*: If there is good reason to suspect that an individual may be at risk of injury due to a particular health problem, medical advice should be sought.

5. *Training*: It is a legal responsibility for all employers to ensure that employees have received manual handling training, which includes the principles of safe manual handling, and training specific to the tasks being carried out and to any equipment used to facilitate the handling.

6. *Load*: If there is concern that the load being handled is heavy or perhaps handled too frequently, the HSE guidelines for assessing the weight risk factor can be used.

Guidance on the Calculation of Risk for Load Weight

Working within the HSE guidelines does not mean the work is safe, just as working outside them does not necessarily mean it is dangerous. The decision whether the work involves risk or not depends on an effective risk assessment.

Note: No attempt should be made to interpret this diagram without reading the text opposite first.

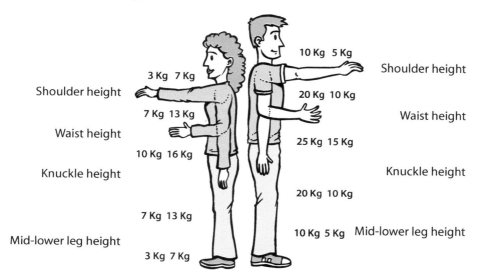

These guidelines assume that the load is easily grasped; handled less than 30 times per hour; and not supported for any length of time. The guidelines also assume that the load is handled by 'average men'; the operation takes place in reasonable working conditions; the lifter is in a stable body position; and there is no twisting, pushing or pulling. **If any of these conditions are not met, then the guideline weights need to be reduced (sometimes substantially).**

Remember: The load needs to be reduced by about one-third to provide the same degree of protection for most women.

The following table contains extra information about how to modify these guidelines when additional risk factors exist:

Additional Risk Factors	Rough Guide
Operation repeated once or twice per minute	Reduce weight by 30 per cent
Operation repeated five to eight times per minute	Reduce weight by 50 per cent
Operation repeated more than 12 times per minute	Reduce weight by 80 per cent
'Average' female	Reduce weight by 30 per cent
Handler twists through 45 degrees	Reduce weight by 10 per cent
Handler twists through 90 degrees	Reduce weight by 20 per cent
Handler seated and twisting	Less than 5 kg
Handler seated	About 5 kg
Pushing or pulling a load (assuming that force is applied with hands between knuckle and shoulder height)	About 25 kg for starting or stopping a load, about 10 kg for keeping a load in motion

Environment

The work environment in which employees are required to carry out manual handling may have a significant impact on their ability to carry out the work safely and the following factors should be considered as part of any manual handling risk assessment:

- Lighting levels
- Thermal conditions (e.g. temperature, relative humidity, ventilation, and weather conditions if tasks are conducted outside)

- Floor surfaces

- Space constraints

- Inadequate access to the load

- General housekeeping

- Noise.

Eliminating/Reducing Risk ✳

Eliminating/reducing the risk associated with manual handling is a major factor for any organisation. The following diagram outlines the system to consider when recommending risk control measures. Elimination or avoidance of risk is the ultimate solution but in many situations this may not be reasonable or practicable. Some control measures may require a combination of engineering and administrative controls.

Hierarchy of Control

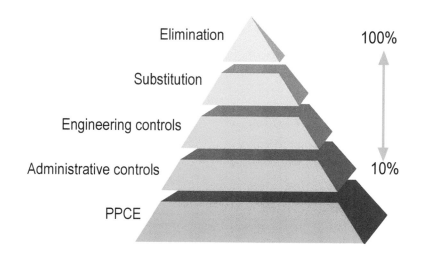

Elimination — 100%

Substitution

Engineering controls

Administrative controls — 10%

PPCE

As indicated by the diagram, elimination of manual handling is 100 per cent effective. On the other hand, manual handling training (administrative control) as an isolated control measure to reduce the risk of musculoskeletal injury is less than 10 per cent effective. Therefore, manual handling training should only be considered as one component of an effective risk management system.

Examples of Risk Elimination/Reduction Solutions

1. *Elimination*: Does the load have to be moved?

2. *Substitution*: Is it possible to purchase 25 kg bags of cement rather than 50 kg bags?

3. *Engineering controls*: Can the workstation be designed to eliminate the need to store equipment above shoulder level? Could a height adjustable pallet truck be used at the end of the production line, which would avoid the need to lift items to a pallet at ground level?

4. *Administrative controls*: Provision of appropriate manual handling training; introduction of a procedure to tag heavy loads; introduction of an employee rotation system from heavy to light duties etc.

5. *PPCE (Personal Protective Clothing and Equipment)*: Provision of safety gloves for carrying hot loads or to protect hands when handling loads that could cause hand injury.

Reducing the Risk of Musculoskeletal Injury

The Task

Is it possible to:

- Improve workplace layout to improve efficiency?

- Reduce the amount of twisting and stooping?

- Avoid lifting from floor level or above shoulder height?

- Avoid or minimise repetitive handling?

- Reduce carrying distances or provide mobile lifting equipment?

- Provide breaks and/or vary work to allow one set of muscles to rest while another is used?

Individual Capacity

Is it possible to:

- Re-design the task and/or the workplace so that a wider range of employees can safely undertake the task?
- Take better care of those who have a physical weakness or are pregnant?
- Give employees more information e.g. about the range of tasks they are likely to face?
- Provide training?
- Is pre-employment screening carried out?

The Load

Can the load be made:

- Lighter or less bulky?
- Easier to grasp?
- More stable?
- Less damaging to hold (have suppliers been asked to help)?

The Working Environment

Is it possible to:

- Remove obstructions to free movement?

- Provide better flooring?

- Avoid steps and steep ramps?

- Prevent extremes of hot and cold?

- Improve lighting?

- Consider less restrictive clothing or PPCE?

Chapter 4

Manual Handling Principles and Techniques

Chapter Outline

- Carry out a range of appropriate manual handling techniques to include lifting, carrying, pushing, pulling, supporting or pulling down of a load by one or more persons.

- Apply the main principles of manual handling to a range of manual handling tasks, with particular emphasis on the need to carry out a personal and dynamic risk assessment to determine if the load can be handled easily.

- Analyse the learners' performance of manual handling techniques.

Lifting an Object

1. *Assess the task, the area and the load*: Use the TILE assessment. Decide on the action required (e.g. load to be lifted or pushed) and know the intended location. To assess the load, push gently using foot or hands/arms.

2. *Establish a broad stable base*: Feet should be shoulder width apart.

3. *Bend the knees*: Bend the knees and lower the trunk. The load of the lift may be assessed at this stage by tilting it.

4. *Ensure good posture*: Maintain natural S-curve of the spine.

5. *Establish and maintain a firm grip*: Grasp the load firmly using full palmar surfaces.

6. *Keep arms close to trunk*: Ensure arms are close to trunk. Lift head and rise avoiding sudden movements.

7. *Keep the weight close to the centre of gravity*: Ensure the weight is close to the body's centre of gravity.

8. *Use feet to change direction*: To prevent injury, use feet to change direction rather than twisting to turn.

NEVER bend over the load that you are lifting.

NEVER bend over with feet placed apart.

NEVER stand too far from the load.

NEVER lift far away from the centre of gravity.

NEVER twist with the load.

NEVER lift with an incorrect grip.

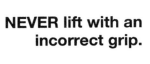

Note: Always remember that if the load is too heavy, get help or use a mechanical aid such as a trolley.

Team Lifting

Apply the same principles as those for a one-person lift; however, for team lifting ensure that the team are of equal height, ability etc. One person should give the instructions. All instructions must be given by the same person throughout the lift and they must ensure that all instructions are clear and precise. Before lifting, both lifters should raise the load slightly to ensure that they are comfortable with the lift.

When preparing to lift, ensure to establish a broad stable base. Ensuring that feet are shoulder width apart, bend the knees and lower the trunk while maintaining good back posture (natural S-curve). Grasp the load firmly using full palmar surfaces. Raise your head and rise without any sudden movements. Once the load is raised, feet should be placed closer together. Incorrect team lifting with twisting and bending of the back may cause serious back injury.

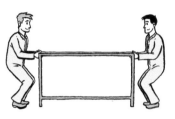

Note: Always remember that if the load is too heavy, get help but make sure that the person is equal in size and ability.

Carrying an Object

To avoid the possibility of pain and/or injury, use the same principles for carrying as for lifting, but also remember that if a load has to be carried, balance the body by carrying two small loads rather than one large one. If the load cannot be divided, hold it close to the body, firmly gripped by both hands. Always ensure a line of vision over the load.

Pulling and Pushing

When pulling a load, place one foot in front of the other. Transfer the weight of the body onto the back leg, ensuring at the same time that the knee is bent slightly, then pull. Maintain a natural S-curve of the back. Stop every few steps, release the load and ensure that the way is clear. Do not twist.

When pushing a load, transfer body weight onto the front leg and move off – again maintain the natural S-curve of the back. It is better to push rather than pull an object as the line of vision is better when pushing and it also exerts less pressure on the back.

Reaching

When reaching, apply the same principles as pushing and pulling above i.e. correct transfer of body weight. Keep knees slightly bent and tuck in the chin. One foot should be slightly to the fore. Place body weight onto the front foot as the load is reached for. Once the load is assessed and ready for retrieval, ensure that a good palmar grip is established. Transfer body weight to the back leg as the load is lifted down. When reaching to place a load onto a shelf, transfer body weight to the front leg.

Manual Handling Risk Assessment Checklists

Task assessed Location(s) Date of assessment	Personnel involved		Assessor's name Signature Date for reassessment
Task	**Hazard present**		**Comments**
	Yes	**No**	
• Does it involve holding loads away from the trunk?			
• Does it involve twisting?			
• Does it involve stooping?			
• Does it involve reaching up?			
• Does it involve large vertical movements?			
• Does it involve strenuous pushing/ pulling?			
• Does it involve repetitive handling?			
• Could the load suddenly move?			
• Is the load shared unevenly between both hands or lifted by one hand only?			
• Is the operator forced to alter their grasp while supporting the load?			
• Could the feet slip?			
Recommendations			

Task	Hazard present		Comments
	Yes	No	
If pushing or pulling: • Are the hands positioned on the item being handled above shoulder height? • Are the hands positioned on the item being handled below the waist? • Is the distance of push/pull excessive? *If carrying:* • Is the distance excessive? • Does the load have to be handled up steps or slopes? *Handling frequency:* • Does the handling frequency require in excess of 12 handling actions per minute? • Does the handling frequency require handling of heavy loads in excess of once per minute? • Are there sufficient rest/recovery periods or changes of activities? • Is the person(s) working under time constraints? • Is any part of the handling event performed while seated? • Are any mechanical aids involved in the handling event? • Does the handling event involve team movement technique?			
Recommendations			

Individual capability	Hazard present		Comments
	Yes	No	
• Does the job require unusual capability? • Does the job present a hazard to those with a health problem? • Does the job present a hazard to those who are pregnant? • Do individuals wear protective clothing or equipment that may increase the risk of performing manual handling operations? • Is manual handling undertaken by individuals who have not received health and safety training?			

Recommendations

The load	Hazard present		Comments
	Yes	No	
• Is the object heavy and does it weigh more than: ~ 5 kg and is it handled from a seated position ~ 16 kg and is it handled in a working posture other than seated ~ 55 kg? • Is it bulky/unwieldy? • Are slippery materials or objects being handled? • Is an awkward grip involved? • Is it difficult to grasp? • Does it have sharp or abrasive edges which contain hot/cold materials? • Can it shift during handling? • Are live animals or persons being moved?			

Recommendations

The work environment	Hazard present		Comments
	Yes	No	

• Are there space constraints preventing good posture?
• Is it necessary to reach over or around obstacles?
• Are there:
  ~ Steps
  ~ Slopes
  ~ Uneven surfaces
  ~ Rubbish piles or clutter
  ~ Housekeeping hazards?
• Is the working environment:
  ~ Too hot (temp. °C____)
  ~ Too cold (temp. °C____)
  ~ Too humid (relative humidity % ____)
  ~ Poorly lit (light level ____ lux)
  ~ Dusty or otherwise obscuring visibility
  ~ Noisy (noise level ____dBA)
  ~ Vibrating
  ~ Dirty
  ~ Odorous
  ~ Windy?			

Recommendations			

Report Summary

Hazards Identified

_____
_____
_____
_____
_____

Breaches of Legal Compliance

_____
_____
_____
_____
_____

Risks

_____
_____
_____
_____
_____

Recommendations to Eliminate/Reduce Risks
(Short term/Medium term/Long term)

_____
_____
_____
_____
_____

Manual Handling Assessment Form

The assessment below relates to the level of competence of an individual on the day of training. An adequate level of supervision and on-going monitoring and refreshing of skills will be required to ensure that standards are maintained.

Name			Instructor
Organisation			Date of training
Skills/techniques*	Competent		Comments
	Y	N	
Lifting to and from ground			
Lifting to and from a bench			
Lifting to and from a height			
Pushing			**Equipment used – pushing/ pulling** Catering trolley ☐ Hand trolley ☐ Other (specify) _____
Pulling			
Team lift			**Equipment used – team lift** Pallet ☐ Table ☐ Other (specify) _____
Lifting bags/sacks (where appropriate)			
Other handling activities (please specify)			

* All shaded skills/techniques must be completed during each manual handling training session.

Detailed Manual Handling Assessment Form

This detailed assessment format can be used as a learning aid to assist manual handling instructors and assessors in competency development during the assessment process.

To be assessed as competent, an individual must be observed applying all eight points.

Name		Instructor	
Organisation		**Date of training**	
Skill	*Assessment*	*Competent*	*Not yet competent*
Lifting to and from the ground	**Did the person:** Y N		
	Assess the task, the area and the load		
	Keep a broad stable base – feet flat on the floor		
	Keep their back straight		
	Bend their knees		
	Have a firm grip		
	Keep their arms in line with their trunk		
	Keep the weight close to the centre of gravity		
	Turn their feet in the direction of movement		

Skill	Assessment			Competent	Not yet competent
Lifting to and from a bench	**Did the person:**	Y	N		
	Assess the task, the area and the load				
	Keep a broad stable base – feet flat on the floor				
	Keep their back straight				
	Bend their knees				
	Have a firm grip				
	Keep their arms in line with their trunk				
	Keep the weight close to the centre of gravity				
	Turn their feet in the direction of movement				
Lifting to and from a height	**Did the person:**	Y	N		
	Assess the task, the area and the load				
	Keep a broad stable base – feet flat on the floor				
	Keep their back straight				

Skill	Assessment	Competent			Not yet competent
	Bend their knees				
	Have a firm grip				
	Keep their arms in line with their trunk				
	Keep the weight close to the centre of gravity				
	Turn their feet in the direction of movement				
Pushing	**Did the person:**	Y	N		
	Assess the task, the area and the load				
	Keep a broad stable base – feet flat on the floor				
	Keep their back straight				
	Bend their knees				
	Have a firm grip				
	Keep their arms in line with their trunk				
	Keep the weight close to the centre of gravity				
	Turn their feet in the direction of movement				

Skill	Assessment			Competent	Not yet competent
Pulling	**Did the person:**	Y	N		
	Assess the task, the area and the load				
	Keep a broad stable base – feet flat on the floor				
	Keep their back straight				
	Bend their knees				
	Have a firm grip				
	Keep their arms in line with their trunk				
	Keep the weight close to the centre of gravity				
	Turn their feet in the direction of movement				
Lifting bags/ sacks (where appropriate)	**Did the person:**	Y	N		
	Assess the task, the area and the load				
	Keep a broad stable base – feet flat on the floor				
	Keep their back straight				

Skill	Assessment	Competent			Not yet competent
	Bend their knees				
	Have a firm grip				
	Keep their arms in line with their trunk				
	Keep the weight close to the centre of gravity				
	Turn their feet in the direction of movement				
Other (please specify)	**Did the person:**	**Y**	**N**		
	Assess the task, the area and the load				
	Keep a broad stable base – feet flat on the floor				
	Keep their back straight				
	Bend their knees				
	Have a firm grip				
	Keep their arms in line with their trunk				
	Keep the weight close to the centre of gravity				
	Turn their feet in the direction of movement				

Manual Handling Frequently Asked Questions

These are the manual handling frequently asked questions as outlined by the Health Service Authority (HSA).

Q. What legislation covers manual handling?

Part II, chapter 4 of the Safety, Health and Welfare at Work (General Applications) Regulations 2007 outlines the requirements that must be adhered to in relation to manual handling. The key requirements include:

1. Carrying out a manual handling risk assessment of existing manual handling tasks before making an informed decision on what manual handling tasks need to be avoided or reduced.

2. Organising tasks to allow the use of mechanical or other means to avoid or reduce the need for the manual handling of loads by employees in the workplace. The hazards can be avoided or reduced through the introduction of appropriate organisational measures, for example the improved layout of a work area to reduce unnecessary long carrying distances, or through the use of appropriate means, in particular mechanical equipment.

3. Providing instruction and training to relevant staff.

Q. Who should be trained?

All employees, including part-time and temporary employees, who carry out manual handling that involves risk, and supervisors/ managers responsible for monitoring manual handling practices.

Q. How many people should be trained in one session?

Ten people per training session is recommended to allow for individual demonstrations and practice.

Q. Do I need to assess every manual handling task?

Manual handling is a physical activity that takes place in every workplace, and in some cases the activity does not pose a problem. However, it can be a potential workplace hazard when an employee is required to handle very heavy loads which could result in a back injury. The type of manual handling activity that needs to be assessed is defined in regulation 68 of the Safety, Health and Welfare at Work (General Application) Regulations 2007:

> Manual handling of loads means any transporting or supporting of a load by one or more employees and includes lifting, putting down, pushing, pulling, carrying or moving a load, **which, by reason of its characteristics or unfavourable ergonomic conditions, involves risk**, particularly of back injury, to employees.

These characteristics or unfavourable ergonomic conditions are the risk factors that are outlined in schedule 3 of the 2007 Regulations and have the potential to cause harm.

The picture across illustrates a manual handling activity that would need to be addressed as part of the manual handling risk assessment process. A characteristic of the load that involves risk is the barrel weighing 80 kg. An unfavourable ergonomic condition is the physical strain involved in having to lift such a load.

Q. Why does manual handling result in a risk of injury or ill health?

Many of the problems that cause back pain are the result of injury and damage to a disc. Bending over results in pressure on the discs and may also cause a disc to bulge backward toward the spine. Twisting and bending together put the greatest stress on the spine, especially on the discs, and is an example of a work condition that increases the risk of back injury. The picture across illustrates some examples of work conditions that involve risk.

Load is too heavy

Body in unstable posture

Difficult to grasp

Q. How do I carry out a risk assessment of manual handling tasks?

Stage 1: This stage involves collecting information on how the task is performed and identifying the key stages in the task. This should be a team effort involving consultation with those that normally do the job. The person carrying out the assessment should have a thorough practical understanding of the type of manual handling tasks being carried out.

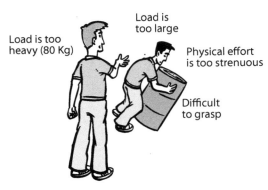

Load is too heavy (80 Kg)

Load is too large

Physical effort is too strenuous

Difficult to grasp

Stage 2: Collect all technical details to include information on load weight, load size, number of manual lifts, postures observed and work environment.

Stage 3: Identify the problems or risk factors. This should be completed by making reference to the risk factors detailed in the HSA publication titled *Guidance on the Management of Manual Handling in the Workplace* or the *Guide to the Safety, Health and Welfare at Work (General Application) Regulations 2007: Chapter 4 of Part 2: Manual Handling of Loads*.

Stage 4: Identify what improvements can be put in place. Once the risk factors have been identified, it is necessary to investigate potential solutions. Examples of efforts that should be made include using mechanical aids; organising the work activity to reduce the need for travelling a long distance; or reducing the size of the load. Clearly document the rationale for deciding on the appropriate control measure, outlining why other control measures were not possible and how the suggested control measure will avoid or reduce the risk of injury. Employees should be consulted as part of this process, and where a new work activity is introduced, it needs to be assessed to ensure that it does not introduce new hazards.

Stage 5: Review the effectiveness of the control measures – effectiveness is the degree to which the control measures have avoided or reduced the risk of injury.

Q. Are there appropriate guidance documents to refer to for advice and direction on how to comply with the Manual Handling of Loads Regulations?

There are three guidance documents available in relation to the Manual Handling of Loads Regulations:

1. *Guide to the Safety, Health and Welfare at Work (General Application) Regulations 2007: Chapter 4 of Part 2: Manual Handling of Loads*

2. *Guidance on the Management of Manual Handling in the Workplace*

3. *Manual Handling Risk Assessment in the Hospitality Sector.*

Q. Is there any guidance document I can refer to for information on the new Manual Handling Training System?

Download *Guidance on the New Manual Handling Training System – 2010 Revision* from the HSA website.

Q. What is the current guidance on course content for a manual handling training course for employees?

Training, and information inclusive, is not enough to ensure safe manual handling but rather is just one important aspect of a manual handling management programme. Training should be specific to the work tasks involved. As there is a wide variety of manual handling tasks, it is impossible to set down a specific training course.

At the end of a training course, participants should have a clear understanding of the risks involved in manual handling and be able to apply the skills learnt to their specific work activities. To do this, it is essential that the course content should include both instruction and practical training, and should cover the following topics:

1. Information on the law relating to manual handling.

2. Information on anatomy and biomechanics of the spine and muscles. This should give training participants a basic understanding of the function of the spine, intervertebral discs, muscles and ligaments, and how certain hazardous postures can contribute to the risk of injury.

3. Guidance on fitness for the task. Written guidance can be given on exercises for flexibility and muscle toning. (Practical exercises for flexibility and muscle toning are outside the scope of occupational manual handling training.) Participants should

not engage in such exercises without consulting a relevant medical professional.

4. Information on the specific manual handling hazards identified in a risk assessment and any possible measures to avoid or reduce manual handling.

5. Information on good handling techniques and practice at applying these techniques.

6. Procedures for dealing with unfamiliar loads.

7. Instruction on appropriate clothing and footwear while handling loads and on PPCE if essential for the work activity.

8. Importance of good housekeeping in relation to providing a safe work environment.

9. Co-operation of trained employees.

Q. How often do employees need refresher training?

Refresher training will be at intervals of not more than every three years and when there is any major change in the work involved or equipment used, or when an employee is transferred to another activity requiring different loads to be handled.

Q. How often do manual handling instructors need refresher training?

Instructors must undergo refresher training at intervals of not more than every five years. (This is changing with the new Manual Handling Training System.)

Q. Are there minimum requirements for the duration of manual handling training courses for employees?

The HSA do not specify time duration for manual training courses. However, the HSA do advocate that course content should reflect topics outlined in the *Guidance on the Management of Manual Handling in the Workplace*. The duration of the training course should be tailored to the number and complexity of the handling procedures being taught. The employer(s) must satisfy themselves that the instructor who delivers the course covers the relevant topics comprehensively.

Chapter 5

Planning and Design of Manual Handling Training Programmes

Chapter Outline

- Develop manual handling training programmes to include lesson plans with clear objectives, appropriate materials and aids to support learning, and strategies to motivate changes in manual handling practice.

- Identify the necessary organisational resources needed to plan and support the delivery of effective manual handling training programmes.

Adult Learning

Learning can be defined as a process through which learners acquire and apply knowledge, skills and attitudes. Learning is a way of inducing change through these three elements:

1. Changes to a learner's **knowledge** can affect the ability to remember and understand information.

2. Changes to a learner's **skills** can affect the ability to analyse, evaluate and apply knowledge; to perform physical tasks; and to display certain behaviours in interacting with others.

3. Changes to a learner's **attitudes** can affect opinions, points of view or outlook held.

Characteristics of Adult Learners

Individuals learn at various rates and in different ways according to their intellectual ability, education level, personality and cognitive learning styles. Teaching strategies must anticipate and accommodate the differing comprehension rates of learners.

Adults learn best in a democratic, participatory and collaborative environment. Adults need to be actively involved in determining how and what they will learn. They need active rather than passive learning experiences.

Adults need to be shown respect and trainers must acknowledge the wealth of experiences that adults bring to the classroom. These adults should be treated as equals in experience and knowledge and allowed to voice their opinions freely in class. A trainer who lectures at the learner causes resentment and frustration.

Adults are practical thinkers and problem-solvers. They are more impatient in the pursuit of learning objectives and less tolerant of work that does not have immediate and direct application to these objectives.

Below is a table outlining the differences between child and adult learners:

Child Learners	Adult Learners
Children feel it is their job to learn.	Adults see themselves as doers, using previous learning to achieve success.
Children have little say in what they learn or in what they are taught.	Adults see the learning process as valuable and relevant in terms of their own development, work, success etc.
Children, as learners in a formal setting, are usually a homogeneous group i.e. approximately the same age.	Adults are very different from each other; adult learning groups are likely to consist of varying education levels, ages and background.

Teaching Adult Learners

Adults learn best when:	Matching adult learning needs with appropriate methods
They feel valued and respected for the experiences and perspectives they bring to the training situation.	Elicit participants' experiences and perspectives through a variety of stimulating activities.
The learning experience is active rather than passive.	Actively engage participants in their learning experience through discussion and a variety of activities.
The learning experience actually fills their immediate needs.	Identify participants' needs and develop training concepts and learning objectives according to these identified needs.
They accept responsibility for their own learning.	Make sure that training content and skills are directly relevant to participants' experiences so that they will want to learn.
Their learning is self-directed and meaningful to them.	Involve participants in deciding on the content and skills that will be covered during the training.
Their learning experience addresses ideas, feelings and actions.	Use multiple training methods that address knowledge, attitudes and skills.
New material relates to what participants already know.	Use training methods that enable participants to establish this relationship and integrate new material.
The learning environment is conducive to learning.	Take measures to ensure that the physical and social environment (training space) is safe, comfortable and enjoyable.
Learning is applied immediately.	Provide opportunities for participants to apply the new information and skills they have learned.
Learning is reinforced.	Use training methods that allow participants to practise new skills and receive prompt, reinforcing feedback.

Learning occurs in small groups.	Use training methods that encourage participants to explore feelings, attitudes and skills with other learners.
The trainer values participants' contributions as both learner and teacher.	Encourage participants to share their expertise and experiences with others in the training.

Motivation

Motivation can be defined as the internal drive directing behaviour toward some end. External forces can influence behaviour but it is the internal force of motivation that sustains behaviour. The sources of motivation are complex and in most cases it is not just one thing that motivates us to learn but a combination of things, such as social relationships, external expectations or parental influences, social welfare, personal advancement, stimulation and cognitive interest/competence.

Motivation is concerned with:

- *Intensity*: Mohammed Ali, 'I was saying "I'm the greatest" long before I believed it.'

- *Direction*: Keep focused. Marcus Aurelius, 'Ask yourself at every moment, "Is this necessary?"'

- *Persistence*: Albert Einstein, 'It is not that I am so smart, it is just that I stay with problems longer.'

Motivation to Learn

Motivation to learn is personal but can be influenced by external factors. Abstract concepts such as attitude and needs are personal and not easy for a trainer to address in motivating the learner. Trainers deal with learners whose needs and motivations are varied. Life experiences widen the gap and create diversity, which is important in learning.

Trainers must meet the challenge of designing resources that are motivating and should address issues such as curiosity, self-efficacy, attitude, need, competence and external motivators. In designing resources trainers must first gain the attention of learners, and provide relevance in what is being taught to the goals and needs of learners so that they can gain confidence as the learning process unfolds, resulting in satisfaction which will provide further motivation to continue learning.

Strategies for Stimulating Motivation	
Gaining and sustaining attention	• Use novel or unexpected approaches. • Stimulate lasting curiosity with problems that invoke mystery. • Vary presentation.
Enhancing relevance	• Have learners determine how learning relates to personal goals. • Provide opportunities for matching previous experiences. • Increase familiarity by building on previous experiences.
Building confidence	• Create positive expectation of success by having clear goals and objectives. • Provide learners with a reasonable degree of control over their own learning.
Generating satisfaction	• Create opportunities for learners to use newly acquired skills. • Use positive symbolic rewards. • Maintain consistent standards and match outcomes to expectations.

Motivational Learning Environment

The following factors are motivating when applied to a learning situation:

1. *Action*: Involves getting learners out of their seats and actively involved in the learning process both mentally and physically.

2. *Fun*: Helps energise learners and provides opportunities for involvement.

3. *Choice*: Provides variety and learner control by using different resources.

4. *Social interaction*: Such as group discussions, workshops, collaborative problem-solving and case studies.

5. *Error tolerance*: Allows learners to feel comfortable in making mistakes and provides opportunities to learn.

6. *Feedback*: Constructive feedback should be continuous, pointing out the positives and focusing on how performance can be improved.

7. *Challenges*: Setting goals that are attainable yet challenging.

8. *Recognition*: Providing for minor as well as major achievements.

Learning Styles

All learners have different intellectual abilities; this means that they think and learn differently. Some learning patterns will have been developed as a result of formative education experience, where materials were presented in a way that benefited learners with linguistic/numerical abilities. As a result, innate learning styles may not have been developed and learners may need to identify their own learning pattern.

There are various ways of classifying differences in learning styles. Many theories and models have been proposed but these are the three most common learning style classifications:

1. Left and right brain

2. Auditory, visual and kinaesthetic

3. Activist, reflector, theorist and pragmatist.

Left and Right Brain

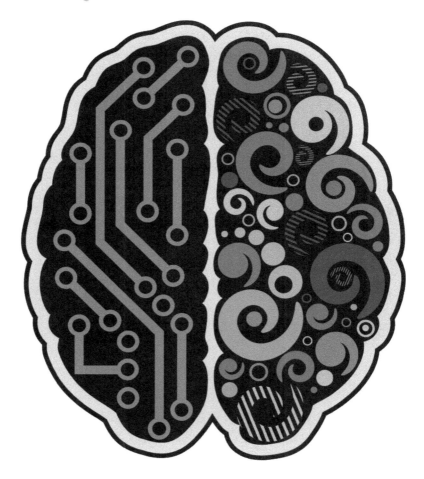

The brain has two distinct sides or hemispheres which process information in different ways. Information is processed using the dominant side. However, the learning and thinking process is enhanced when both sides of the brain participate in a balanced manner. The left brain processes information in a linear, sequential, logical manner while the right side is intuitive.

Left Brain	Right Brain
Logical	Creative
Linear	Holistic
Sequential	Random
Concrete	Symbolic
Analytical	Intuitive
Verbal	Non-verbal
Reality-based	Fantasy-oriented

Trainers encourage learners to use both sides of the brain. Experiments have shown that people who have been trained to use one side of the brain more than the other (accountants and engineers versus artists and musicians) find it difficult to 'switch' when necessary. When the weaker side is stimulated and encouraged to co-operate with the stronger side, there is greater synergy. For example, Newton understood the theory of gravity while day-dreaming.

Trainers should combine analytical exercises with creative, expressive activities. Because people can store information in the left and the right brain in the form of pictures (V), words (H) or sensations and feelings (F), trainers must give multi-channel messages. This means giving colourful visual back-up to verbal messages at the same time as appealing to learners' emotions and senses. These messages can be stored simultaneously in several parts of the left and the right brain and therefore multiply the chances of recall.

Visual, Auditory and Kinaesthetic Learning

Research by neuro-linguistic programming experts Bandler and Grinder has identified three distinct communication and learning styles:

1. Visual learners
2. Auditory learners
3. Kinaesthetic (tactile) learners.

Visual learners: These learners relate more effectively to written information, notes, diagrams and pictures. They need to see body language and facial expression to fully understand the content of the lesson. Visual learners also like to take detailed notes to absorb the information. Visual learners make up about 65 per cent of the population.

Auditory learners: These learners learn best through verbal lectures, discussions, talking through and listening to what is said. They understand underlying meanings of speech through listening to tone of voice, pitch, speed and other nuances. Auditory learners make up about 30 per cent of the population.

Kinaesthetic learners: These learners learn effectively through touch, movement and space, and learn skills by imitation and practice. They learn best through a hands-on approach. Kinaesthetic learners make up about 5 per cent of the population.

While all people utilise all three types of learning, most people display a preference for one over the other two.

Activist, Reflector, Theorist and Pragmatist

Honey and Mumford's Learning Styles Model and Learning Styles Questionnaire have become widely acknowledged in the training and development field. Referring to Kolb's Learning Cycle, they suggest that learners have preferred learning styles i.e. a preference to spending more time in one part of the cycle than in another. It is critical for the trainer to know this for both one-to-one training situations and group situations, and to develop their delivery style accordingly.

Kolb's Learning Cycle

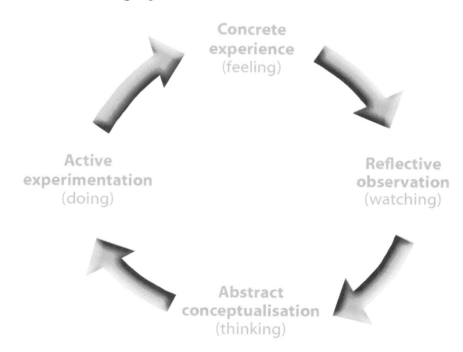

Concrete experience (feeling)

Reflective observation (watching)

Abstract conceptualisation (thinking)

Active experimentation (doing)

In practice, a group of learners will have a combination of preferences, while individual training must be designed to be flexible to accommodate the learner's preference and still achieve the desired result. It is also important that the trainer knows their own preferred learning style as they are likely to want to deliver training on this basis which may not suit the learner.

Learning Styles Questionnaire

Learning Styles Questionnaire		
If you agree more than you disagree with the statement, put a √ in the box. If you disagree more than you agree, put an X in the box. Be sure to mark each item with a √ or X.		
1.	☐	I often act without considering the possible consequences.
2.	☐	I like the sort of work where I have time for preparation and implementation.
3.	☐	I have strong beliefs about what is right and wrong, good and bad.
4.	☐	I have a reputation for saying what I think.
5.	☐	I believe that formal procedures and policies restrict people.
6.	☐	I take pride in doing a thorough job.
7.	☐	I tend to solve problems using a step-by-step approach.
8.	☐	What matters most is whether something works in practice.
9.	☐	I often find that actions based on feelings are as sound as those based on careful thought.
10.	☐	I take care over the interpretation of data available to me and avoid jumping to conclusions.
11.	☐	I question people about their basic assumptions.
12.	☐	When I hear about a new idea or approach I immediately start working out how to apply it in practice.

13.	☐	I actively seek out new experiences.
14.	☐	I like to reach a decision carefully after weighing up many alternatives.
15.	☐	I am keen on self-discipline such as watching my diet, taking regular exercise and sticking to a fixed routine.
16.	☐	I accept and stick to laid-down procedures and policies so long as I regard them as an efficient way of getting the job done.
17.	☐	I am attracted more to novel, unusual ideas than to practical ones.
18.	☐	I pay meticulous attention to detail before coming to a conclusion.
19.	☐	I get on best with logical, analytical people and less well with spontaneous people.
20.	☐	In discussions I like to get straight to the point.
21.	☐	I thrive on the challenge of tackling something new and different.
22.	☐	I am careful not to jump to conclusions quickly.
23.	☐	I do not like disorganised things and prefer to fit things into a coherent pattern.
24.	☐	I believe in coming to the point immediately.
25.	☐	I enjoy fun-loving, spontaneous people.
26.	☐	I prefer to have as many sources of information as possible.
27.	☐	I like to relate my actions to a general principle.
28.	☐	I tend to be attracted to techniques such as network analysis and flow charts.
29.	☐	I tend to be open about how I am feeling.
30.	☐	I listen to other people's points of view before putting mine forward.
31.	☐	I tend to have distant rather than formal relations with people at work.
32.	☐	I tend to judge people's ideas on their practical merits.

33.	☐	I prefer to respond to events on a spontaneous basis rather than plans things out.
34.	☐	In discussion I enjoy watching the manoeuvrings of other participants.
35.	☐	I find it difficult to produce ideas on impulse.
36.	☐	In meetings I put forward practical ideas.
37.	☐	Quiet, thoughtful people tend to make me feel uneasy.
38.	☐	It worries me if I have to rush out a piece of work to meet a deadline.
39.	☐	Flippant people usually irritate me.
40.	☐	I can often see better, more practical ways to get things done.
41.	☐	It is more important to enjoy the present moment than to think about the past or future.
42.	☐	I get irritated by people who want to rush things.
43.	☐	I tend to be a perfectionist.
44.	☐	I think written reports should be short and to the point.
45.	☐	In discussion I usually produce spontaneous ideas.
46.	☐	I think decisions based on a thorough analysis are sounder than those based on intuition.
47.	☐	I can often see inconsistencies and weaknesses in other people's arguments.
48.	☐	I like people who approach things realistically.
49.	☐	More often than not rules are there to be broken.
50.	☐	I prefer to stand back from a situation and consider all the perspectives.
51.	☐	I believe that rational, logical thinking should win the day.
52.	☐	In discussions I get impatient with irrelevances and digressions.
53.	☐	On balance I talk more than I listen.
54.	☐	I tend to discuss specific things rather than engage in social discussion.

55.	☐	I am keen to reach answers via a logical approach.
56.	☐	I am keen to try things out to see if they work in practice.
57.	☐	I enjoy being the one that talks a lot.
58.	☐	If I have a report to write I tend to produce lots of drafts before the final version.
59.	☐	In discussions with people I often find I am the most dispassionate and objective.
60.	☐	In discussions I often find I am the realist.
61.	☐	When things go wrong I am happy to shrug it off and put it down to experience.
62.	☐	I like to ponder many alternatives before I make my mind up.
63.	☐	I like to be able to relate current actions to the bigger picture.
64.	☐	I tend to reject spontaneous ideas as being impractical.
65.	☐	I find the formality of having objectives and plans stifling.
66.	☐	In discussions I am more likely to adopt a low profile.
67.	☐	I tend to be tough on people who find it difficult to adopt a logical approach.
68.	☐	Most times I believe the end justifies the means.
69.	☐	I am usually one of the people who puts life into a party.
70.	☐	It is best to think carefully before taking action.
71.	☐	I am keen on exploring the assumptions, principles and theories underpinning events.
72.	☐	I do not mind hurting people's feelings as long as the job gets done.
73.	☐	I quickly get bored with methodical, detailed work.
74.	☐	On balance I do the listening rather than the talking.
75.	☐	I like meetings to be run along methodical lines.

76.	☐	I do whatever is expedient to get the job done.
77.	☐	I enjoy the drama or excitement of a crisis situation.
78.	☐	I am always interested in finding out what people think.
79.	☐	I steer clear of subjective or ambiguous topics.
80.	☐	People often find me insensitive to their feelings.

Score Key

For each question you have ticked on the questionnaire sheet, put a tick in the box beside the question number on this sheet. Add up the ticks in each column.

☐	1.	☐	2.	☐	3.	☐	4.
☐	5.	☐	6.	☐	7.	☐	8.
☐	9.	☐	10.	☐	11.	☐	12.
☐	13.	☐	14.	☐	15.	☐	16.
☐	17.	☐	18.	☐	19.	☐	20.
☐	21.	☐	22.	☐	23.	☐	24.
☐	25.	☐	26.	☐	27.	☐	28.
☐	29.	☐	30.	☐	31.	☐	32.
☐	33.	☐	34.	☐	35.	☐	36.
☐	37.	☐	38.	☐	39.	☐	40.
☐	41.	☐	42.	☐	43.	☐	44.
☐	45.	☐	46.	☐	47.	☐	48.
☐	49.	☐	50.	☐	51.	☐	52.
☐	53.	☐	54.	☐	55.	☐	56.

☐	57.	☐	58.	☐	59.	☐	60.
☐	61.	☐	62.	☐	63.	☐	64.
☐	65.	☐	66.	☐	67.	☐	68.
☐	69.	☐	70.	☐	71.	☐	72.
☐	73.	☐	74.	☐	75.	☐	76.
☐	77.	☐	78.	☐	79.	☐	80.
Total ☐ **Activist**		**Total** ☐ **Reflector**		**Total** ☐ **Theorist**		**Total** ☐ **Pragmatist**	

Understanding Your Learning Style

Use the general norms below, which are based on the scores obtained by well over a thousand people, to plot your own learning style.

	Very Strong Preference	**Strong Preference**	**Moderate Preference**	**Low Preference**	**Very Low Preference**
Activist	13–20	11–12	7–10	4–6	0–3
Reflector	18–20	15–17	12–14	9–11	0–8
Theorist	16–20	14–15	11–13	8–10	0–7
Pragmatist	17–20	15–16	12–14	9–11	0–8

The Pros and Cons of Each Learning Style

The following tables look at the pros and cons of each learning style in broad terms. Note that these are general tendencies; each individual is different and may exhibit different styles, depending on the situation. In an ideal world learners would have no particular general preference for one style over another and would drift in and out of different styles to suit the situation.

The Activist

The good	The not so good ...
· Flexible and open-minded · Happy to have a go · Happy to be exposed to new situations · Optimistic about anything new · Unlikely to resist change	· Tendency to take the immediately obvious action without thinking · Takes unnecessary risks · Tendency to do too much themselves and hog the limelight · Gets bored with implementation

The Reflector

The good	The not so good ...
· Careful · Thorough and methodical · Thoughtful · Good at listening to others and assimilating information · Rarely jumps to conclusions	· Tendency to hold back from direct participation · Slow to make up their minds and reach a decision · Tendency to be too cautious and not take enough risks · Not assertive or forthcoming – no 'small talk'

The Theorist

The good	The not so good ...
• Logical 'vertical' thinkers • Rational and objective • Good at asking probing questions • Disciplined approach	• Restricted in lateral thinking • Low tolerance for uncertainty, disorder and ambiguity • Intolerant of anything subjective or intuitive • Full of 'should, oughts and musts'

The Pragmatist

The good	The not so good ...
• Keen to test things out in practice • Practical, down to earth, realistic • Business-like, gets straight to the point • Technique-orientated	• Tendency to reject anything without an obvious application • Not very interested in theory or basic principles • Tendency to seize on the first expedient solution • On balance task-orientated, not people-orientated

Tips for Delivering Training to the Different Styles

The trainer should be flexible and equally able to deliver training to any of the four styles; very often a combination of them all. The table below lists some tips that will help to accommodate each style. In general, many of the tips will need to be incorporated in a training programme to satisfy the needs of all learners.

Tips for Gearing Training or Presentations to the Activist	
Make the session interactive	Encourage the learner to ask questions, give inputs etc.
	Provide learners with opportunities for 'hands-on' activities.
Ask questions of the individual/audience	Keep the learner active by asking questions.
	In a group context open the questions to the group or direct specific questions at particular individuals who are vocal or seem to be knowledgeable.
Have breakout or group sessions	Where appropriate, split the group into teams of 3, 4 or 5 people and give clear instructions on what they have to discuss and what is expected of them.
Provide things to keep them occupied	Always keep the activist busy; use all available time for practice.
	Bring along samples of your work, e.g. promotional posters and completed forms, and pass them around the group.
Other	

Tips for Gearing Training or Presentations to the Reflector	
Do a review of the skills demonstration or presentation at the end	Make it interesting by asking the learner/audience to help with the review.
	Ask open questions as a review activity.
Identify the reflectors	Ask simple questions to ascertain the style of the learner or if possible have them complete the Learning Styles Questionnaire.
	In a group context, try to identify the reflectors in the group and mix them with activists if using breakout groups.
Use case studies	Where appropriate, use case studies where the individual/group has to solve the problems and make recommendations.
Other	

Tips for Gearing Training or Presentations to the Theorist	
Ask theoretical and fact-based questions	For example: • What do you think would happen if . . .? • Does anyone know the . . .?
Ask for the learners' opinions on suggestions made in the presentation	For example: • So, do you think this would work? • What do you think would be the pitfalls of this approach?
Other	

Tips for Gearing Training or Presentations to the Pragmatist	
Keep the training/presentation moving along	Pragmatists will get impatient with extended talking/discussion.
Give practical examples of how your suggestions will work	For example: • X has used this approach and the results have been . . .
Other	

It is important to remember that the learning styles should be taken as a guideline only. Trainers have preferred styles of learning (and delivering training) so care must be taken to ensure that personal preferences and bias are not reflected in the method of training delivery. This should always be considered from an effective learning perspective and in line with the needs of learners.

Barriers to Learning

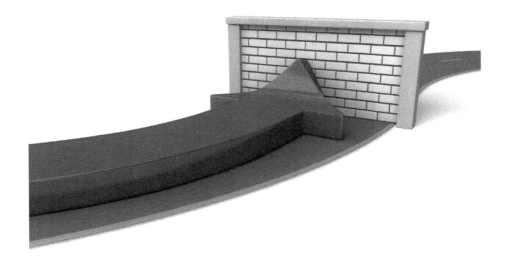

There are specific barriers to learning in an adult context that the trainer needs to be aware of and understand. These barriers will differ from learner to learner, situation to situation, and organisation to organisation, but can be categorised as:

1. Emotional

2. Organisational

3. Environmental.

Emotional barriers: Emotional barriers are individual to the learner or sometimes to a group if they have shared common experiences. Feelings such as 'I'm not good enough' or memories of a less than happy childhood education impinge upon learning. Lack of confidence, fear of exposure in front of the group, and feeling too old to learn are all emotional barriers to learning.

Organisational barriers: This can include a culture that does not value learning. It can manifest itself as an attitude of 'just get on with the job' or as a culture of defensiveness which discourages learners or employees from trying new ideas or attending training. Likewise, a lack of procedures to support training and learning on the job would be an organisational barrier.

Environmental barriers: Environmental barriers are a hazard for in-company training as the location may not be conducive to learning or there may be interruptions. Noise levels, lighting, temperature and other physical elements need to be right or they will present a challenge to both trainer and learner alike.

TASK

Outline your own experiences regarding barriers to learning. Consider emotional, organisational and environmental barriers.

Outline solutions to the following common barriers to learning:

- *Motivation* – how to improve the ambitions of learners to engage with learning.

- *Access* – how can access barriers, such as availability and location, be overcome?

- *Finance* – how can learning be financed without bias?

- *Time* – how to target provision at those who have little time in which they can learn.

- *Concerns over quality* – how to ensure learners have access to quality learning.

Aims and Objectives

An **aim** is a general statement of intent from the standpoint of the trainer; it states what they intend to do during a lesson, session or course. It does not try to be specific in terms of outcomes. Remember that each learner participating in a course is different and may have various reasons for being there so the overall aim should be meaningful to the majority of the target audience.

Examples of course aims may be to:

- Improve learner knowledge of training and development.
- Increase the computer literacy of learners within the group.
- Ensure that learners know how and why to lift safely.

A course may have more than one aim, particularly if it is of a lengthy duration, but the training specialist should be able to limit it to two or three, otherwise it may be confusing and a possible indication that the programme or course is trying to 'catch all' rather than be specific.

An **objective** is more specific and written from the standpoint of the learner. It is used to describe the results or outcome of a learning activity and should tell exactly what the learner will be able to do at the end of the training.

Typically, an objective is structured by using three elements:

1. Performance that is required or will be achieved.

2. The conditions under which it will be achieved.

3. Standard that it will be achieved to.

These elements can be all explicit or it may be appropriate to make one or two implicit, providing that it does not lead to ambiguity for the intended audience. For example, the time element can be implicit if the course objectives start with the phrase: 'At the end of the course ....' This indicates that the time to achieve the required standard is the duration of the course.

In one-on-one skills training (on-the-job training), this would not be appropriate and a more explicit objective may be required, which clearly contains all three elements. For example, 'At the end of this session, you will be able to clean the vacuum chamber within 30 minutes and achieve a particle reading of less than 0.01 per cent.' Clearly, the detail of the objective depends on the type of training, the nature of the business, the criticality of the process, the target audience and so on.

Needless to say, it is generally good practice to specify objectives for both trainer and learner alike. Some of the practical reasons why objectives are specified are listed below:

- Limit the task to remove difficulties of interpretation.

- Enable trainers to determine priorities.

- Enable trainers to select the most appropriate approach and method.

- Ensure measurement is possible so that the effectiveness of the learning experience can be judged.

- Permit adaptation for different situations more easily.

Some of the more common words used in writing objectives are listed below; they are typically action-orientated verbs and are particularly useful for writing skill-based objectives.

Action-orientated Words for Writing Objectives for Skills Training			
Write	Select	Construct	Demonstrate
Develop	Record	Identify	

Note: 'Skills' is sometimes referred to as 'psychomotor' in training terms.

Words for Writing Knowledge Objectives			
State	Define	List	Know
Understand			

Note: 'Knowledge' is sometimes referred to as 'cognitive' in training terms.

Words for Writing Attitude Objectives			
State	Define	List	Know
Understand			

Note: 'Attitude' is sometimes referred to as 'affective' in training terms.

The SMART model for writing objectives, especially for individuals, should also be employed:

1. Specific

2. Measurable

3. Achievable

4. Realistic

5. Time based.

Chapter 6

Delivery of Manual Handling Training

Chapter Outline

- Deliver effective manual handling training programmes using a range of tools and techniques, including managing group dynamics.

- Demonstrate an understanding of adult learning principles and the need for effective communication skills.

- Give effective vocal instruction in practical manual handling techniques.

Role of Trainer

The effective transfer of training and learning depends on the trainer because it is only the trainer who can remove the mental blocks of the learner, motivate the learner to learn, and delete the negative perception the learner may have regarding the training. A lot can depend on the personality of the trainer also.

A trainer's performance can be measured on three dimensions:

1. **Knowledge and experience**: Technical competence in subject matter being taught; practical 'on-the-job' (OTJ) experience; academic qualifications; knowledge of the training function; and competence in promoting training.

2. **Trainer skills**: Training Needs Analysis; applying learning theory to course design; keeping trainer recall high; making learning fun; performing (voice control, eye contact, body language etc.); developing and using audio-visual support; leading discussions; creating and conducting exercises; and training evaluation.

3. **Concern and availability**: Empathy; listening skills; asking and answering questions; dealing with 'difficult' learners; facilitating; and adapting style and content to fit the learners' needs.

TASK

Evaluate the effectiveness of your own performance under the following headings: knowledge and experience; skills; concern and availability.

Communication

Communication is concerned with more than just the words that are used. Tone of voice, facial expression and body language all play a major role in how a person is understood. If a person is communicating in a situation where it is not possible to use all these elements to enhance the message, awareness and care need to be taken.

In 1967 Albert Mehrabian considered the relative importance of three elements in communication: words, tone of voice and facial expression. He suggested that whenever a person communicates:

1.   7 per cent of the communication is in the words that are spoken.

2.   38 per cent of the communication is in the tonality (how the words are said).

3.   55 per cent of the communication is in physiology or body language.

Therefore, a huge amount of what is said is conveyed by non-verbal or subconscious routes. Incongruous tone or body language may be an indicator that the trainer does not mean what is said or at least is not comfortable with the spoken word.

Importance of First Impression

1.   How the learner is greeted and how the initial 'message' is conveyed can set the tone of the course.

2.   Use eye contact to 'read' faces. This is an excellent technique for establishing rapport, detecting understanding or confusion and getting feedback.

3. Use positive facial expressions to aid in the process of communication.

4. Walk about the room as a point is being made. A skilled trainer co-ordinates movements and gestures with instructional delivery. Be energetic.

5. Walk toward learners as they respond to questions or make comments. A slow nodding of the head while maintaining eye contact demonstrates interest and encourages active learner involvement.

6. Avoid distracting gestures or body language, such as excessive pacing, jingling keys and playing with a pen.

7. Limit the use of desks or lecterns that establish an artificial barrier between the trainer and learner.

8. Display enthusiasm about the topic and its importance. Energy and excitement are contagious and directly affect the enthusiasm of learners.

Group Learning

Delivering training in a group setting, such as classroom-based training, is quite different to delivering training in an OTJ-based scenario. Issues of group dynamics, individual needs, fears, and matching of learners are all critical in a group scenario, while location and access to resources may be prevalent in an OTJ setting. Good communication skills are relevant to both scenarios.

Presence

The trainer must establish and maintain their presence from the moment the learners enter the learning centre.

Preparation	Delivery
Make the room 'yours'. Ensure tables and chairs are arranged suitably; prepare a welcome message on the flipchart or on the presentation; play suitable invigorating music; and have materials set up and on display.	**Use the room.** Keep learners interested by physically using the room. Try not to be rooted to one place; practise moving around while delivering the key message, making sure to establish eye contact with all present in the process.
Create curiosity!	**Body language.** Standing establishes presence, especially if the learners are sitting; the professional trainer soon gets used to being on their feet all day! However, it is also appropriate to sit during open discussions, group feedback sessions and other situations to convey a more relaxed atmosphere or to blend into the general group rather than obviously being the 'trainer'.
Greet the learners. Be there early to meet each person individually as they arrive, introducing yourself and making a point of using their name.	
Know the learners. If possible, get to know some basic information about the learner (name, experience etc.) in advance of the course; this is useful both practically (like having prepared name tags) and for pitching delivery. It can help in establishing presence and shows preparation.	**Use your voice.** Place emphasis on key words; vary tone, pitch and speed as appropriate; and speak clearly so that everyone hears. Together with the use of hands, posture etc., voice is perhaps the most effective delivery tool a person has, and it is a major factor in defining presence.

Knowledge of the Material

The trainer is often the subject expert so knowledge is not an issue. The ability to transfer learning effectively is what makes a subject expert into an expert trainer, and the following are some tools or techniques that can help in a practical way.

Item	Notes
Trainer guide	In an ideal world the trainer will have received a train-the-trainer session for the class/workshop/presentation and will have a trainer guide. This is often in the form of a presentation with accompanying notes, a session plan etc., but it is also useful for having extra notes beyond the published content of the training programme. Use the guide as an active document during delivery, consulting it as appropriate to help stay on track, have useful facts at fingertips etc.
Research	Research for useful articles on the subject and have printed copies if relevant. Keep an eye on media for articles and journals for up-to-date theory, models and best practice.
Other	

Handling a Group

The trainer's ability to handle group situations and dynamics is a key competency for any effective trainer when delivering to more than two people. The following table highlights some of the key techniques to support this competency.

Technique	Notes
Establish ground rules	Prevention is better than cure and the establishment of a clear set of ground rules early on in the training is the best way to prevent misunderstandings; set boundaries; clarify issues; and establish a code of conduct.
Mix and match learners	Learners on a training course will generally sit beside people they know or work with but this may not be good for them or the course dynamic. Think about having set places prepared in advance or let it happen naturally via an ice-breaking activity.
	Learners in a learning event can learn a lot from each other: think about mixing and matching learners into groups based on experience, organisation, personality type, learning style etc.
Dealing with difficult learners	The trainer may have any number of scenarios presented to them which represent a challenge to their delivery.
	Learners who are there because they 'were told to', learners who are resistant to change, learners who bring 'gripes' into the learning environment, and the 'expert': all require the trainer to be able to respond appropriately in a way that is unique to the situation.

TASK

Note your observations on how a trainer can deal appropriately with these common scenarios: the expert; the 'not interested'; the griper; the 'too old to learn'; the quiet one; the joker; other.

Managing the Activities

The trainer must be alert at all times and this can be exhausting. Focusing on managing activities can save the trainer a lot of energy which could be used for other more stressful purposes. The following table suggests techniques for enhancing this competency.

Managing Activities	Tips and Techniques
Clear instructions for group work	When setting out group work, make sure that the instructions clearly set out what is to be done; how it is to be done; what the expected outcome is; and the time allowed for the activity. It might be necessary at this stage for the trainer to specify if they want to see roles being taken on by the team. It is helpful to issue clear, printed instructions, either on a handout or projected as part of the presentation.
Discussions	Discussions are very useful within a course and promote the sharing of knowledge. However, the trainer must be skilled in controlling the discussion so that it stays on track, is relevant and has an outcome. The trainer might decide to sit down during a discussion, as this gives an open signal to the group. It has the added advantage in that it provides the trainer with the opportunity to bring the discussion to a close by standing.
Individual work	Be clear on assigning individual work, such as multiple choice lists and questionnaires. Issue clear instructions and indicate trainer assistance if it is available; if books can be consulted etc.
Demonstrations	If giving a demonstration in front of a group, planning is essential. Is a volunteer needed during it or should one be agreed in advance? What could go wrong and what can be done to avert it? Are all the necessary materials/resources to hand? When using a member of the group for demonstration purposes, make sure to have their full permission and co-operation.

Keeping on Track

Keeping a training event on track can be a major challenge, yet it is imperative that the learners meet the stated objectives. The following items will assist the trainer to keep on track.

Item	Notes
Prepare a session plan	A session can be a classroom-based training event or part thereof; a specific skills training activity as part of a larger job training plan; or any other training event with a specified beginning, end and outcomes.
	Create templates for various types of training sessions and make sure to include:
	• Clear, well-written aims and objectives.
	• Start times, break times, end times, and the suggested time and duration of each individual activity.
	• Trainer activity – what exactly is the trainer doing during the session/ activity e.g. presentation, facilitating a discussion or group work?
	• Trainer/learner activity – what are the learners doing and what is the expected outcome during each part of the session?
	• Equipment – ensure that necessary equipment and tools are available and that there is a sufficient amount e.g. markers and paper.
Logistics	The trainer should ensure that they know in advance the time and location of lunch, as well as the time it takes to get to and from the venue. Will there be a queue? Will it be a 'first-come, first served' basis or can food be pre-ordered and brought to a reserved area?
	What time does the training venue close? If there is more than one day to the event, can time be saved setting up for the days (unless another training event is sharing the venue after/before)?
Other	

Supplying Appropriate Examples and Anecdotes

An experienced trainer will have plenty of examples, stories, sayings and anecdotes. More importantly, they will have the ability to encourage the learners to share their stories with the group and manage the process so that the learners keep on track.

Ability to Give and Receive Feedback

Good communication skills for giving and receiving feedback are essential in any training profession. The ability to give and receive feedback is critical to both group and individual skills training sessions. Some of the more common tools and techniques of this competency are noted below.

1. *Use questions*: The trainer should have a set of questions prepared for various scenarios. For example, the trainer has instructed the group to work in teams to practise skills covered and to make a brief presentation to the larger group on their findings. Using prepared questions can elicit further learning from the exercise, as well as give feedback on their work.

2. *Feedback*: Feedback should always be constructive. The following are basic rules for giving feedback: (a) be specific and concrete; (b) avoid being judgmental; (c) encourage questions – make it two-way; (d) do not overload – too many items will discourage the group and the message will be diluted; (e) focus on the positive and be constructive when feeding back on areas or suggestions for improvement; and (f) always thank the group for their work and encourage appreciation from the rest of the group.

3. *Encourage consistently*: Use words/phrases that encourage the group, but be wary of doing it habitually – it may seem

programmed and therefore not sincere. A simple 'well done' or 'excellent work', coupled with saying things like 'the experience in this group is fantastic', can create a feeling of wellbeing among learners and motivates them to keep up the learning.

Remember that body language is important too and should mirror what the trainer is saying, as should tone of voice.

Individual or OTJ Training

Much of the material from the group section can be equally applied to individual or OTJ training situations. There are some key differences listed below.

Presence

Establishing presence with an individual in an OTJ setting can be a lot 'softer' than is necessary in a group context. Suggestions to help this process include:

1. Finding out about the learner in advance (background, experience etc.) and using this to create rapport in early conversation.

2. Telling them about one's own self and background.

3. Setting aside specific time at the beginning of the training or during a coffee break, without the disruption or interruptions of the workplace.

4. Setting out clearly the trainer's role as the facilitator of learning, the administrator of assessments etc. Explaining the approach toward feedback and the context in which it will be done.

Knowledge of the Material

The trainer needs to be competent in the skill that they are delivering so it is important to be up to date with new procedures and processes, best practice, new personnel or organisational changes.

Handling Different Learners

The trainer must be flexible in order to be able to adapt their delivery to meet the needs of the learner, not the other way around. Just as with groups, individual learners may have bad experiences of learning from a previous job or have fears of inadequacy. Ensure that the training is geared toward the learner's preferred style; that choices are given; and always give the 'big picture' – the 'why' to support the 'how'.

Managing the Activities

Training in an OTJ context can be a lot more challenging for a trainer than showing up at a venue to deliver group training. Issues such as space for training, dealing with interruptions, having a dedicated training computers system, and negotiating with other departments or units for access to required resources are all part and parcel of delivering OTJ training.

Keeping on Track

Adult learning theory suggests that the trainer should give the adult choices about how training is delivered and in what order, and to apply assessment when the learner states that they are ready. Yet the trainer also has a requirement to keep on track and complete the training by a specified time. How is this achieved?

Proper and complete preparation is the key to success: have daily, weekly and individual session plans ready but be prepared to change them if necessary. Production pressures may prevent the completion of a particular skills training session so have a back-up plan ready that does not depend on the other planned session being complete.

Supplying Appropriate Examples and Anecdotes

The trainer should have stories but should also collect stories from other more experienced personnel in the same job and from others outside of the organisation. Ask the learner for examples also and create analogies and comparisons between what is being taught and other everyday events and situations.

Ability to Give and Receive Feedback

This competency needs to be further refined when dealing with an individual learner. The basic rules still apply but also consider the following points:

1. *Focus on the behaviour, not the person*: Use neutral language instead of making it personal e.g. 'Step 2 was performed incorrectly, which led to ... let's try again ....' This is more effective than 'you did step 2 wrong'.

2. *Be specific*: Refine the feedback, 'In step 2 I noticed you ... which led to ....'

3. *Share ideas and information*: Use opportunities for feedback to share ideas and information. For example, 'That's actually good that you didn't get it right the first time; some people do and we lose a valuable opportunity to learn from it. Let me tell you what happened the last time ....'

4. *Give feedback to help the learner*: Ensure that the feedback is always given to help the learner in a constructive and friendly way.

5. *Own it*: Be sincere with feedback. If something is done wrong, say it. If it needs to be done faster, say it. If you are concerned with progress, say it. But always say it sensitively with encouragement, compassion and with an underlying message of help and assistance. Do not opt out and say that someone else observed the action or behaviour.

6. *Timing*: The timing for giving feedback is important. Feedback should be given as soon as possible after the event and should not be mixed with other messages. For example, try not to mix positive and negative messages together as the positive one may lose its meaning in the process.

Course/Programme Design

It is beyond the scope of this course to go into the detail of instructional design but below are some basic principles to be followed.

Learning Principles

Ensure to follow the principles of **adult learning** as discussed. Vary the content to suit the needs of the four **learning styles**. Mix practical exercises with theory, introduce examples and provide time for reflection and note-taking.

Target Audience

Consider the **background** of the audience – what is the experience level of learners or is it a mixture? Should a minimum entry requirement be set or is the course open to all? Consider **motivation** – are the learners going to the training of their own free will or is it something that they 'have to do'? What is the WIIFM (What's In It For Me) for each learner?

Organisational Constraints

Will there be pressure on learners to keep an eye on work issues and therefore be distracted from time to time? Does time present a practical problem? Perhaps the training should be delivered outside the normal working hours, provided that the learners are adequately compensated. Will there be access to required resources that are needed to deliver the training effectively?

Other Methods

Experience shows that learners learn better when having **fun**, so try to introduce humour where possible. **Accelerated learning** is a particular method of training delivery that utilises people's natural inclinations and abilities and engages the senses in an active way. The trainer should explore this innovative learning technique and introduce it into sessions.

Motivation of Learners

Learners will have varying levels of motivation depending on their particular circumstances. Highly motivated learners can become demotivated because of a staid delivery. The trainer should keep delivery interesting using a variety of techniques.

Visual Aids

PowerPoint is the most used training tool and can be very effective; however, there is a tendency to overuse this method of delivery to such an extent that the aid becomes the presentation rather than the presentation being the aid. A few tips for using PowerPoint include keying large legible letters and having at least one image on each slide, using colour and the KISS (keep it simple, stupid) mnemonic. When using flip charts, writing should be attractive, big and bold, using capital keywords. Use symbols and frames to accentuate and tear off sheets for display.

Remember that as a trainer YOU are the presentation, guide, tutor, storyteller and expert. The trainer is the principal medium for learning transfer; everything else plays a supporting role.

Varying Pitch, Pace and Tone of Voice

A trainer that delivers in monotone will lose their audience. Even the most enthusiastic of learners will eventually become bored and will begin to drift off. It is possible, within reason, to keep everyone's attention by varying pitch, pace and tone of voice. Be excited and animated when appropriate, leave gaps so that the important messages sink in and emphasise key words or phrases by repeating them if necessary.

Introduce Humour

Not everyone is blessed with the wit of a comedian but everyone has a sense of humour. Find your humour and introduce it appropriately. There is nothing like a light moment, when everyone laughs or smiles, to create a positive atmosphere in a training room. Not everyone is the humorous type so games and activities that encourage learners to have fun can be introduced instead.

Vary Activities

A good training event will have a variety of activities, from group exercises to individual tests; action learning sessions to sedentary work; and role plays to observing videos. Variety is the spice of life and variety spices up a training event too. When a trainer is disciplined and prepares for sessions by writing or typing out a session plan, they will see whether the training event is varied enough to have a fighting chance of keeping everyone happy all of the time.

Tips for Trainers

Every trainer develops their own style as they progress through their career and it is important to note that this is perhaps the most important factor in learning transfer. A trainer who is an expert in their field and has charisma and an ability to engage with their audience will probably gain better results than a trainer who is going through a checklist of the 'right' things to do in a training event. Trying to keep too many balls in the air might end up being counter-productive.

Useful tips to turn a good training event into an unforgettable one:

Tips	Notes
Use the room	Move around as much as possible and try not to be tied to a laptop or projector.
Make eye contact with everyone all of the time	Consciously make an effort to engage every learner with appropriate eye contact. This will help people feel included and has the added benefit of keeping their attention. Be careful not to focus on any one individual too much.
Ask questions	There is a lot of expertise and experience in the room – use it. Ask prepared questions to open up discussion and promote the sharing of knowledge.
Tell stories	Everyone loves a story. Be confident to share a personal experience; show how you learnt from your mistakes and got to where you are. Do not feel pressured to always be the expert.
Use silence	Some trainers feel that they have to constantly 'perform'. Silence is allowed and is necessary to allow space for learners to think of answers to questions and questions to have answered.
Other	

Personal and Practical Considerations

Dealing with nervousness can be stressful. Practise the presentation beforehand. It may feel a little silly doing it in front of the bathroom mirror but practice makes perfect. In particular, rehearse the beginning of the presentation over and over. If extremely nervous, it is a good idea to memorise the first five minutes. The first five to ten minutes are usually the worst but once the session gets going the speaker becomes less nervous.

Remember to breathe! Breathe deeply because when people are nervous their breathing is generally too shallow. Breathing slowly and deeply improves the flow of oxygen into the body and thus the flow of blood to the brain.
This will help a person to think more clearly and to order their thoughts. Taking in more oxygen also improves the flow of air to the vocal chords, allowing the person to speak clearly, thereby reducing nervousness and helping them to remain calm.

 Remember the expectant attitude: if a person thinks of themselves giving an excellent presentation, they probably will.

Develop checklists and management plans to ensure that equipment, material or aids are not forgotten.

 Arrive early so that you have time to settle in.

Check all the support equipment before the presentation so that everything is in working order.

 Make sure that notes, slides etc. are in order and easily accessible.

Create a physical setting with which you are comfortable.

Warm up your voice before the start of the presentation. Talk to the participants before the presentation starts. If this is not possible, sing or hum to yourself!

If there is a need to sit in front of the group before presenting (e.g. if team presenting), try some simple, unobtrusive isometric exercises. Remember that no one will know that they are being done.

Use adrenalin to advantage. With practice, anxiety can look like and become enthusiasm.

Move around and do not become rooted to the spot.

Develop your own style of presentation. A teaching or presenting style is an extension of personality. There is no one right style, but there is a style that is right for you.

Vocal Awareness for Trainers

Trainers use every means of communication to deliver courses effectively and a key tool at their disposal is their voice. If people like the sound of what they hear, it will help them 'buy in' to what is being said and help maintain interest. Research shows that an audience picks up five times as much from the voice compared with the actual words being spoken, so expanding range of tone, volume and pitch, for example, can be powerful for any communicator.

Also, anyone who spends several hours a day speaking – sometimes in stressful situations because they are on show and have to project a confident image – can get serious voice muscle fatigue. Occupational voice problems have already appeared in the teaching profession and many teachers have had to take time off or retire early because of them.

So knowing a few techniques on how to care for the voice can be invaluable and applicable to anyone who is working in an occupation that carries a high voice loading, including lecturers, professional speakers, aerobic instructors and even bingo callers.

Healthy Vocal Habits

Most of the time, it is assumed that the voice just 'works' by itself and does not need any special care. In fact the human voice is remarkably resilient and it is only when problems are experienced that people get worried and want to know what to do. Yet there is no doubt that prevention is always better than cure. Below are a number of areas that impact on the quality of your voice.

Breathing: The first area to look at is the pattern of breathing. Breathing is involuntary so it is seldom given much thought.

However, there is a proper way to breathe: it should be relaxed and rhythmic. Centred breathing will support the voice. Poor breathing technique is a common problem. When a person is anxious, it is an automatic response to take shorter, shallower breaths. In fact the opposite is required: a person should always try to breathe long and deep – it is an instant way to calm down.

Try this exercise

To increase breath control, begin by breathing in for three counts and out for six counts. Establish this as a breathing pattern and try to do ten repeats. When this is comfortable, breathe in for four counts and out for eight. Gradually add sounds to the outward breath, for example counting, speaking your name and address, or a line from a poem or story.

Posture: Posture affects the quality of a person's voice. When standing, balance the body's weight evenly, and keep feet hip-width apart and pointing forward. Aim to maintain a flexible and well-balanced neck, drop the shoulders and relax the arms – swing them backward and forward a few times. Avoid leaning forward and straining with the neck or chin. An imbalance in posture can set up tensions in the body.

Warm-ups: Like any physical activity, the muscles involved in speech need warming up to prevent injury. Athletes and instrumentalists know that it is wise to warm up before competing to improve performance and reduce the risk of injury, and it is the same with the intricate muscles of the voice. Warming up may seem unnecessary but a tired, husky sound or painful throat often indicates that the voice has been overused.

Make vocal workouts part of a working routine at the start of each day to keep the voice tuned and healthy. Finding time to do some gentle warm-ups pays off dramatically in the long run. Nothing fancy is required – just some sound work after the breathing. The warm-ups need only take five minutes in the morning. They can calm a person down and get them breathing in a natural way. They will also get all the speech organs moving and working before the speaker faces an audience for the day, ensuring that the first words come out with confidence.

Try this exercise

Go through all the vowels and 'sing' them while breathing out. Try saying tongue twisters as well. Next, imagine the most enormous sticky toffee in your mouth and imagine chewing it very hard. Make really exaggerated chewing movements, including getting it stuck on the roof of your mouth and in your teeth!

Pitch: The speaker should use their natural pitch; one that is comfortable and fits their own vocal instrument. The 'hum' pitch – expressing mild surprise – is the pitch at which a speaker should be speaking. Trying to change the natural speaking voice, for example continually pushing it down to be more authoritarian, dropping it to appear gentler or raising it in an effort to be heard, can cause vocal damage.

Stress: A common cause of voice strain is stress and often it is not even realised. Basically, the voice needs several different parts of the body to function well. Like breathing and posture mentioned above, another vital concern for the voice is the jaw. The jaw is a very strong hinge which gets used thousands of times each day. Sometimes it gets tired and rebels, and when this happens, the muscles become very tense and the whole of the bottom half of the face begins to hurt.

Try these exercises

1. An instant remedy to stress is to drop the jaw. It relaxes all the facial muscles and gives everything a moment to recover.

2. Taking time to go through breathing and relaxation exercises will sort out most cases of tense jaw.

3. Stretching the neck and shoulders will promote good breathing and posture habits, and it will relieve tension.

Environment: Spending time in smoky environments can be very damaging to the voice; there is really nothing that harms the voice as much as regular exposure to cigarette smoke. If a training session has to be delivered in a noisy environment, the speaker may find a situation where they need to raise their voice to be heard, which can cause some strain. Extreme temperature changes can also occasionally cause voice strain. If there is a need to speak outside, always wear a scarf and try to keep the neck warm.

Drinking habits: If the speaker knows that they are going to do a lot of talking, either professionally or socially, it is a good idea to have a large glass of water to hand. Do not wait to become thirsty or for the voice to feel dry. It is impossible to speak clearly with a dry throat, and it could cause strain and damage if attempted. The voice works better when the vocal chords are kept moist and the mucus in the vocal system is thin. Vocal chords vibrate against each other hundreds of times per second and require constant lubrication.

> **Try this solution**
>
> Drink as many as ten to 12 glasses of fluid each day. Juices and herbal teas are fine. However, avoid iced water. Also avoid drinks that include caffeine, such as tea, coffee and coke, because these are diuretic (water-expelling). They dehydrate instead of rehydrate. If caffeine is a must to get going, then re-fill the mug afterwards with water and drink it all.

One final point …: Vocal folds become swollen when a person has a cold, sore throat or laryngitis, and this makes the voice deeper or huskier. It may be tempting to chat but it is important to remember that the voice is now especially vulnerable to damage. Extra care is needed when these illnesses occur.

Speaking to Large Groups

One area that learners often ask trainers about is how to make their voices louder, particularly those about to address a large group. It is also interesting that the inability to hear what is being said comes top of the list of complaints about any speaking and listening situation. Volume is not about how loud the voice is but about how far it travels. It is the combination of working on more breath, more energy and slightly lowering the pitch that will result in good voice control and help to fine-tune volume.

Remember that volume needs adjusting all the time, even within the same sentence. This is partly to add variety for the listener and also to aid the sense of what is being said. The speaker should train themselves to be sensitive to each situation so that they are aware of when they need to turn it up, turn it down or turn it off! Starting sentences very quietly almost certainly ensures that the listener will miss the first few words. This may be crucial information (such as who the speaker is), so be absolutely sure to begin and end on a strong note.

Techniques to Make the Voice Seem Louder

The key is to use the mouth energetically to produce more sound without shouting. For example:

1. Aim your voice forward.

2. Imagine a mask on your face and speaking into its mouthpiece.

3. Next, aim to a point in the room, then to the far wall in the room.

4. Finally, and still without shouting, practise at home by going outside and aiming for the back wall of the garden!

A fuller voice produces more volume than a thin, reedy one. This may mean aiming for a lower note. Using as much breath as possible behind each phrase will help to strengthen and fill out the voice. Finally, pay special attention to sentence endings; this is when many people find their voice tails off. Make a point of finishing on a strong note.

It is a fair statement that most people take their voice for granted, rarely considering the need to look after it and thinking even less about how it works. However, trainers need to pay some attention to what is, after all, one of their primary work tools. As with other work tools, they should know how to look after it so that they always get the best from it. If the trainer is to learn how to look after and maintain their voice, and know what to do when something goes wrong with it, then it makes sense to also know how it works.

How the Voice Works

Voice is stimulated by an impulse from the brain by an intention to speak. Once this has occurred, there are three main elements involved in the production of sound: air flow, vibration and resonators.

Air Flow (The Respiratory System)

Air enters the body through the nose and mouth and then passes down the windpipe (or trachea) into the lungs. This inhaled air, which supplies oxygen to the body, travels through the ribcage, causing this dome-like diaphragm to expand. Exhaled air returns up the trachea and encounters the larynx. By using the breathing muscles of the ribcage, back and abdomen, the body controls the stream of air pressure. This can be likened to the power supply of the voice. Breath is needed to begin the sound process (try closing your mouth and pinching your nose — it is impossible to make any sound).

Vibration (Oscillator)

As the exhaled air encounters closed vocal folds in the voice box in the throat, in overcoming their resistance, it causes them to vibrate and make a sound like air escaping from the neck of a balloon as it deflates. This is where the voice is formed. When the voice is used, two bands of muscular tissue in the larynx are closed (the vocal folds) across the air flow. There are about 30 muscles within and around the larynx that function together to move and adjust the vocal folds. Depending on age, sex and health, the folds may open and close between 60 to 1,000 times per second. The primary function of the voice box is to serve as a protective valve for the airway. This vibration can be felt by placing a hand gently on the neck and saying a sentence out loud.

Resonators (Cavities)

Resonators give richness of sound to the voice. The sound waves produced by the folds are only a buzz, although it has a variable pitch. The rest of the vocal tract modifies the sound, which is turned into speech by movements of the various structures in the mouth (tongue, jaw, palate and teeth), throat, nose and sinuses, to give each individual sound a unique and recognisably different vocal profile. Resonance refers to the shaping of sound waves within a chamber to produce a particular sound output and is also modified by the shape of the chest or physical build and eating habits. It is by managing and manipulating the resonant qualities in these spaces that subtle variations in the tone of the voice can be made, carrying power (projection), flexibility and range of voice. For example:

- By relaxing the tongue and expanding the throat, a generous resonating space can be created.
- By dropping the jaw and shaping the mouth, the voice can be carried further without strain.
- By focusing the tone of the voice into the front of the face, the voice will be amplified.

In the first few moments of any training course, when the scene is being set for the course, delegates will already be forming an impression about whether the trainer is worth listening to, so never forget the instant impact of the voice and remember that tone speaks volumes.

Voice Problems

Does this story sound familiar? You have been providing training for two days and there are still two more days to do this week before the end of the course. Your throat is starting to feel sore. You need help. What should you do? What should you not do? The first thing to do is to stop talking! Make it clear to anyone around that you have hurt your voice and are going to rest it. If it is possible, leave work and cancel social engagements, then lie down in a warm, quiet room. Even half an hour of this can be a great help.

The late Larry Hagman, otherwise known as J. R. Ewing from the long-running TV programme *Dallas*, said in an interview on BBC Radio 4's *Woman's Hour* that he used to have 'silent Sundays' when he was filming in order to save his voice for the rest of the week. It may not be possible to follow his particular advice, but there are plenty of things that can be done (and a couple that should not) to cosset and help the voice recover, and to keep it at its best.

Do these:

- Make sure to drink plenty of fluids. Try hot water on its own or with lemon and honey.

- Soothe the airway by inhaling steam. Spend extra time in the shower or in a steam-room when the voice is tired or when fighting a cold or other temporary irritation. Steam soothes and moistens the larynx.

- If there is any tension of the head, spine, shoulders or jaw, try to release it through gentle exercise, massage or relaxation.

- If speaking at an important event, consider using voice amplification.

Do not do these:

- Whisper to save the voice. This is the one remedy that most people frequently resort to for relief but it tires the voice and may lead to further damage.

- Repeated throat clearing. Try sipping water instead to clear the mucus.

Take care when using gargles or throat pastilles that promise to relieve pain, unless prescribed by a doctor. They can provide temporary relief but many contain chemicals, such as menthol, that dry out the mucous membranes in the throat and larynx, dull the throat so that the pain is not felt and make the vocal folds more vulnerable to irritation and infection. Painkilling lozenges can also mask pain and increase the risk of overuse injury.

Similarly, if suffering from a cold or flu, be cautious with over-the-counter medications that offer to dry up symptoms. If they dry the cold, they also dry the vocal folds. Be wary of analgesics.

Try using a hot drink of honey and lemon or sucking glycerine-based lozenges, fruit pastilles or chewing gum to help stimulate saliva and keep the mouth and throat moist and more comfortable.

Remember that vocal damage might not be felt for several hours after it has occurred. This is because the voice box has less nerve sensation than other parts of the body so it is not that easy to receive a warning that damage is occurring. A useful self-check of whether or not the voice is hurt is to say very quietly and gently the 'ha' sound. If the voice cord is swollen, the voice wavers more than usual.

If a voice problem lasts for more than two weeks, seek medical attention – do not put it off. The sooner the problem is dealt with, the greater the chance of a full recovery. Many young singers in pop and rock bands do long-term damage to their voices because they strain them and then ignore the symptoms.

Analysing the Voice

A handy tool to use to assess the voice is the Voice Value VOICES acronym, which looks at six different dimensions of the voice: volume, on/off, intonation, colour, extras and speed.

Volume (projection): This has nothing to do with shouting; it is all about using the voice to its full capacity, combining energy, controlled breathing and facial muscles. Practise speaking at different levels as if addressing the front, middle and back rows in a theatre.

On/off (diction): Remembering to pay attention to the beginnings and endings of words ensures crisp, clear delivery. Tongue twisters, nonsense rhymes and pop songs are good to practise with.

Intonation (tone and pitch): This is where the audience decides within the first 30 seconds of the training programme how much attention they are going to pay to the rest. It is very important to 'pitch' it correctly – no one likes a harsh or sarcastic tone and everyone responds better when genuine rapport has been established.

Colour (expression): Changing how a person sounds gives variety to voice. It is tiring to listen to the same level of voice for long periods of time. Learning how to add expression keeps listeners engaged and on their toes throughout the day. Use nursery rhymes and try saying them in a variety of ways. The best way to improve expression is to read to small children – you can really ham it up and they love it!

Extras (fillers – 'err', 'uhm', 'y'know', 'well', 'right'): These detract from the content of the programme and make delegates feel uneasy and embarrassed. It is worth learning to pause instead. This commands instant attention and gives the speaker time to plan the next word or phrase without sounding uncertain.

Speed: There is nothing guaranteed to make people switch off more than someone speaking so fast it is impossible to keep up with them. The listener stops trying after a few sentences and their attention is then very difficult to win back. As a rule of thumb – if asked to repeat something more than twice in a short burst of speaking (say, two minutes' worth), then the speaker probably needs to pay attention to volume, diction or speed.

A simple action plan for the speaker to get to know their own voice would be to send themselves regular voicemails, then focusing on one aspect each week. Within six weeks the speaker will have a better understanding of their own voice.

Appendix

Civil Liability for Manual Handling

Manual handling accounts for up to 30 per cent of accidents reported annually to the HSA. Therefore, it is not surprising that there have been a large number of civil claims concerning manual handling.[1] These claims mirror the various elements of the requirements in the Manual Handling Regulations 2007 and can be categorised under the following headings:

1. Mechanisation of manual handling

2. Alternative methods maintained in working order

3. Absence of training and mechanical aids

4. Manual handling procedures, including training, in line with 'best practice' as published by reputable organisations

5. Training in safe handling techniques provided and kept up to date

6. The relevance of the statutory Regulations

7. Self-employed persons can be sued

---

1. The HSA has published a detailed analysis of the costs of manual handling incidents in the healthcare sector, including claim costs: *Analysis of the Causes and Costs of Manual Handling Incidents in the Health Care Sector* (2007), available at www.hsa.ie

8. Limits to liability

9. Manual handling and human rights.

Mechanisation of Manual Handling

In *Hurley* v *Imokilly Co-Operative Creamery Ltd*,[2] Mr Hurley's job involved tipping large milk churns into tanks, which he did manually. One day he injured his back doing this. Expert evidence given on his behalf in court showed that other creameries had investigated mechanical devices with which employees grabbed the neck of the churns. This would take away a good deal of the burden of the churns' weight. Because the creamery in this case had not followed this alternative approach, the Supreme Court decided that it had not provided a safe working environment for Mr Hurley and that it had been negligent. He was therefore entitled to compensation, which in today's terms amounted to about €50,000. As noted earlier, the 2007 Regulations (and the 1993 Regulations before them) also require employers to investigate methods of reducing the risk associated with manual handling.

Maintenance of Mechanised Systems

In *Dunleavy* v *Glen Abbey Ltd*,[3] Mr Dunleavy was a warehouse employee of Glen Abbey Ltd. The company had bought a fork-lift truck so that Mr Dunleavy would take deliveries into the warehouse without having to lift or carry them manually. As a result of this, the company did not give manual handling training to Mr Dunleavy. Unfortunately, the fork-lift truck regularly broke down, a fact about

---

2. Supreme Court, 1972

3. [1992] ILRM 1

which Mr Dunleavy regularly complained to the company. The result was that Mr Dunleavy still spent time carrying and lifting loads into the warehouse.

One day nine cartons of metal fasteners arrived at the company's premises in a van on a pallet. Mr Dunleavy went for the fork-lift truck to lift the cartons from the van but its battery was dead. Mr Dunleavy then proceeded to lift the cartons manually from the van with the help of the van driver. Each carton was small, about 57 cm x 24 cm x 23 cm, and weighed between 35 kg and 42 kg. This was below the maximum weights specified in the Manual Handling Regulations 1972,[4] the Regulations which applied at the time. The two men lifted four of the cartons in this way, but when they were lifting the fifth carton the van driver let go. Mr Dunleavy was jerked by the weight and he suffered a back injury. He claimed damages in negligence and breach of statutory duty.

Although the company had provided a fork-lift truck for Mr Dunleavy, the High Court judge held that this was not sufficient because it regularly broke down. The company should have foreseen that Mr Dunleavy would have to continue to lift items manually into the warehouse. He had not been provided with manual handling training as required by the Manual Handling Regulations 1972. The High Court judge therefore found that the company was in breach of its statutory duty to Mr Dunleavy. The judge pointed out that training would have brought home the dangers of manual handling to Mr Dunleavy, and that he might have decided not to have lifted the load with the driver, so that the breach of statutory duty was

4. The Factories (Manual Labour) (Maximum Weights and Transport) Regulations 1972 (SI No. 283 of 1972), made under the Factories Act 1955

connected to the injury sustained.[5] In this case, because the back injury was not severe, £15,000 (€19,000) compensation was awarded. The case underlines the need to ensure that mechanised alternatives to manual handling are maintained in working order.

Absence of Training and Mechanical Aids

White v *Mid-Western Health Board*[6] concerned an incident in 1987 when the plaintiff, a hospital attendant, was helping to lift a patient weighing about 14 stone (89 kg) from his bed into a chair. The plaintiff and a nurse faced the patient and placed their arms under his shoulders to lift him; the patient slipped and the plaintiff used her full weight to prevent him falling onto the floor. The plaintiff suffered an injury to her shoulder.

The High Court judge noted that: (a) the plaintiff had not been trained or instructed in proper lifting procedures; and (b) *The Handling of Patients: A Guide for Nurses* (published in 1987 by the National Back Pain Association and Royal College of Nurses in England) warned against lifting in the way the patient was lifted in the present case. He also noted that, in the absence of a hoist, more assistance in lifting patients had been recommended by the specialist witnesses in the case. In any event, he noted that, in the absence of a hoist, the procedure should have been carried out only by trained personnel. On this basis, he concluded that the Health Board, as employer, had failed to take reasonable care of the plaintiff. For her injuries that were going to be permanent, he awarded £79,882 (€101,000).

---

5. If it is known that, for example, the absence of training would not have had an impact on preventing a particular injury, a civil claim for compensation will be dismissed even if there has been a breach of statutory duty.

6. High Court, 1993

Manual Handling Training and 'Best Practice'

Kirby v *South Eastern Health Board*[7] involved an incident in January 1988. The plaintiff, a full-time temporary nurse employed by the defendant Health Board, was required to turn a hospital patient, who weighed just under nine stone (57 kg), with another nurse. Both nurses went to opposite sides of the patient's bed and then clasped their hands under the patient. At a given signal, the patient was lifted and the plaintiff was required to stretch across the bed to turn the patient to the far side of the bed. The plaintiff claimed that, in the immediate aftermath of this turning procedure, she noticed a pain in her neck, which later radiated down her body and legs. The plaintiff claimed that the procedure caused her to sustain the injury and that the defendant was negligent in allowing her to perform the turning in the manner outlined.

Evidence from an expert in lifting procedures was that this turning procedure had been recognised as being dangerous by the nursing profession in the late 1970s and early 1980s and that attention was drawn to this in a number of publications prior to January 1988, including the 1987 *The Handling of Patients: A Guide for Nurses* (discussed in the White case, above). The expert also stated that by 1985 the Southern Health Board had issued instructions for the training of nurses which condemned this procedure on the ground that it exposed the nurse who was moving the patient away from her to the danger of back injury.

The High Court judge decided that, having regard to the evidence, the defendant was negligent in that it knew or ought to have known, by the exercise of reasonable care, that this turning procedure was

7.   High Court, 1993

dangerous and steps should have been taken to warn the nursing staff and to ensure that it was not used. Although there was some dispute regarding the medical evidence, he concluded that the balance of evidence supported the view that the plaintiff suffered the injury in the immediate aftermath of the turning procedure. As to contributory negligence, the judge concluded that, as the plaintiff was at all times employed by the defendant and could not reasonably have been aware, without instructions from the defendant of the danger involved in the turning procedure, there could be no finding of contributory negligence. A total of £156,978 in damages was awarded, of which £65,000 was general damages for pain and suffering.

Training Not Updated

In *Firth* v *South Eastern Health Board*,[8] the plaintiff was a ward attendant employed by the defendant board at a hospital which catered largely for long-term geriatric and psychiatric patients. She had joined the staff in 1970 and worked almost continuously at the hospital from then until December 1990 when she sustained a back injury while lifting a patient. In 1970 she had been shown how to lift patients by the then matron of the hospital, but had not received any further training in patient lifting.

On the night of the back injury, the plaintiff was preparing to lift a patient of about 11 stone (70 kg) with the staff nurse on duty. The technique used, described as the orthodox or cradle lift, was that the plaintiff intertwined her right arm through the patient's left arm from under the armpit downwards until she was in a position to

---

8.   High Court, 1994

grip the patient's wrist from the inside. The staff nurse adopted a similar position on the other side. Then both of them put their arms under the plaintiff's thighs or buttocks to form a cradle lift. The lift then commenced with the intention of moving the patient around and upwards on the bed and also of centralising him. Just after the lift commenced, as the patient was being lifted away from the plaintiff and as she was bent inwards over the bed, she felt a severe pain in her lower back and left side and was forced to let go of the patient.

On the technique used, evidence was given that Cork Regional Hospital had published a pamphlet on patient handling in 1985, in which it stated that the orthodox or cradle lift should be avoided whenever possible. Reference was also made to the 1987 *Handling of Patients: A Guide for Nurses* (see the *White* case, above) which had recommended a total ban on the cradle lift. As it involved bending over the patient, the lifting fulcrum was moved away from the lifter's body and it was not possible for the lifter to keep her back straight. Expert evidence was also given in the case that patients should be lifted close to the body of the lifter and that, in the present case, the draw sheet under the patient should have been used to move him in the bed. The expert witness also stated that in her opinion the plaintiff and other staff should have been retrained in lifting techniques from time to time as the training given in 1970 had become obsolete.

The High Court judge concluded that the hospital had been negligent as it had failed to keep up to date with training techniques and had failed to retrain staff, and had therefore exposed the plaintiff to an unreasonable risk of back injury. The injuries sustained by the plaintiff meant that she was unable to return to her work and she continued to suffer severe pain despite a number of operations and painkilling treatments. She was severely restricted in her movements and was unable to walk for long periods. Taking account of future loss of earnings and also the pain she suffered, the total damages awarded in the case was £135,658 (£60,000 of this being general damages for pain and suffering).

The Relevance of the Statutory Regulations

In the *Dunleavy* case, above, the Manual Handling Regulations 1972 were applied in deciding liability. Since their replacement, the Manual Handling Regulations 1993 have also been applied. It is likely that the 2007 Regulations will feature in future cases.

In *Gorry v British Midland Airways Ltd*,[9] the plaintiff was a baggage handler at Dublin Airport. He had begun work with the company in 1990. In 1993 he had been shown a 15-minute video on manual handling techniques. The evidence indicated that there was little other training in manual handling. In October 1996 he was attempting to lift a bag from the baggage carousel. He wrenched his arm and shoulder, and his injuries caused him to be out of work for four weeks. He was symptom-free after two years.

The bag was particularly heavy but was not marked as such, although 'heavy bag' tags were given by the company to check-in staff. The evidence indicated that these were not always used. Expert evidence for the plaintiff stated that training should consist of theory, demonstration and practice, followed by a test of knowledge. Reference was made to the requirements of the Manual Handling Regulations 1993. The Circuit Court judge, Judge Dunne, held

---

9. (1999) 17 ILT 224; Circuit Court, 16 April 1999

that the company had not taken all reasonable precautions. The provision of training, tagging of bags, and accident records were inadequate. She noted that even where people were performing a task regularly, they got into bad habits and needed to be reminded from time to time of how to complete their tasks safely. She held that it was clear that this had not been done here and that the training provided was inadequate. As the plaintiff had fully recovered by 1998, she awarded £6,000 in general damages.

In *O'Connor* v *North Eastern Health Board*,[10] the plaintiff was a general porter in Louth County Hospital, assigned as a medical attendant to a surgical ward. A confused elderly patient weighing about 13 stone (82 kg) had almost fallen out of his bed and the plaintiff had attempted to move him back into position on the bed. The bed was 27 inches (69 cm) high and there was a cot side of a further three inches (8 cm) over which the plaintiff was leaning at the time. He had to straighten his knees, extend and twist his back across the bed and extend his arms at the same time. In the process he felt something 'go in his back' and he later developed extensive back pain and headaches. The plaintiff had not been provided with training in manual lifting.

The High Court judge found that the activity in this case was ergonomically unsound and that the Health Board was in breach of Regulation 13 of the 1993 Regulations, which required the employer to provide training in manual handling.[11] The judge held that, because the patient was about to fall from the bed and the

---

10. High Court, 1999

11. On the changes concerning training in manual handling in the 2007 Regulations, see the discussion above.

165

plaintiff was therefore faced with an immediate emergency, the plaintiff was not contributory negligent in failing to call for help from the nursing staff. The injuries sustained by the plaintiff meant that he would not be able to return to work involving manual lifting. Total general damages were £112,000; special damages, including loss of earnings, were £145,500, making a total award of £257,500.

Self-employed Persons Can Be Sued

In *Allen v Ó Súilleabháin and the Mid-Western Health Board*,[12] the plaintiff injured her back in October 1989 while working as a student midwife in a hospital owned and administered by the Mid-Western Health Board. She was 25 at the time. The first defendant, the senior obstetrician, was attempting a delivery by vacuum and forceps, and instructed the plaintiff to hold the patient's right leg up. The patient's left leg was more stable as it was draped over the shoulder of a male doctor. The patient was in great pain and was pushing downwards and making strong and unpredictable movements with her right leg. The procedure lasted for approximately 20 minutes.

The plaintiff twisted her back during the procedure and she suffered a prolapsed L4/5 disc. The senior obstetrician stated that he had decided that the patient's legs should be held, rather than placed in stirrups, in order to flex the legs as much as possible and thus widen the vagina. He had not been aware that the plaintiff was in pain and if he had seen problems, he would have replaced her with another nurse.

In the High Court the judge held that it was foreseeable that the procedure might take as long as 20 minutes and that the plaintiff

---

12. High Court, 1995; Supreme Court, 1997

was at more risk of injury than the male doctor holding the other leg. The senior obstetrician, as manager of the hospital, owed the plaintiff a duty to provide and maintain a proper system of work. The Health Board, while not an employer of the plaintiff, also owed her a duty and should have established a system to deal with these foreseeable problems. Having chosen not to use stirrups, the defendants should have ensured that a proper system of work was used and that each person holding a leg could be relieved if they were under any strain. The two defendants were both held negligent and as it was difficult to apportion blame, the court assessed liability at 50 per cent each. As to whether there was contributory negligence, the judge decided that it would have been extremely cheeky of the plaintiff to have complained to the consultant obstetrician when he was attempting a delivery. He concluded that she had not been contributory negligent in carrying on as best she could.

The plaintiff underwent surgery but the pain recurred and then worsened. She had two epidural injections but had not benefited. She had tried to continue nursing after the accident but had been unable to do so. She also had to leave university in the final year of a business degree because of pain, particularly when she stood. At the time of the High Court hearing, the pain was virtually constant. The plaintiff was unable to stand for more than five minutes or to walk for more than 30 minutes at a very slow pace. She had no social life and was taking anti-depressants. In the High Court she was awarded £468,363 damages, comprising: £189,520 for loss of future earnings, £23,843 for loss of pension, £50,000 for medical and other expenses, and £205,000 general damages for pain and suffering. The Supreme Court reduced the amount of general damages to £125,000 so that the final total award was circa £375,000.

Limits to Liability: Employee Carelessness and Appropriate Training

All the cases discussed above involved imposing liability on the employer but, as with other areas, not all claims are successful. The following two cases indicate that employers will not be liable where an employee engages in an unsafe procedure where the workplace is otherwise reasonably safe or where the employer has provided adequate training.

In terms of an unsafe procedure, in *Bowdren* v *Southern Health Board*,[13] the plaintiff was employed by the defendant Health Board in the Archives Office of Cork Regional Hospital. He was required to place hospital records on shelves and remove these where necessary. When the plaintiff used the steps provided for his use, the height of the top shelf in the office was at or just above his eye level. There was a clearance of 17 inches (43 cm) between the top shelf and the ceiling. The weight of documents and X-ray photographs, which the plaintiff lifted onto and off the shelves, was approximately 28 lb (13 kg). The shelves were overcrowded and when replacing X-ray photographs onto the top shelf, the plaintiff was required to shove or squeeze them to find space. On one occasion in November 1987, he felt a pulling sensation in his back while working on the top shelf in the Archives Office, but worked until the end of his shift and later that night went to his GP stating that his back injury occurred that day.

The High Court judge held that the defendant board was not liable. He noted that although there was some difficulty for the plaintiff arising from the overcrowded files, work on the top shelf did not involve any stretching upwards, and that there was very little that

---

13. High Court, 1993

was unusually or particularly stressful to give rise to concern or anxiety even in the most prudent and careful employer. While he acknowledged that the weight of some loads might be a factor in back injuries, the plaintiff was lifting approximately 28 lb which was far below the maximum weight in the Manual Handling Regulations 1972 (even if they applied to the plaintiff[14]), and the defendant could not in those circumstances be regarded as negligent. On this basis, the claim was dismissed.

As to the adequacy of training, in *Delaney* v *United Frames Ltd*,[15] the training provided by the defendant was deemed to be reasonable. The plaintiff began working for the company in 1989, where she assembled picture frames. She placed glass panes on a table along with hard-board backing and then clipped the components together. In 1992 she was placing five glass panels, about 50 cm x 70 cm each, onto the table and, in the course of putting them down, she sustained a back injury. She accepted that she could have done the work by lifting one glass pane at a time but she preferred to lift about five or six at a time. She claimed that she had not received adequate training in manual handling and that the system of work was unsafe.

The company had engaged physiotherapists to train employees, including the plaintiff, in lifting techniques. This had included showing a video followed by a practical demonstration on lifting boxes as well as lifting glass from crates. The plaintiff's engineer accepted that the system of work was standard in the industry and that the

14. The 1972 Regulations, made under the Factories Act 1955, did not apply to employees in a hospital. Note also the accident occurred in 1987, before the Manual Handling Regulations 1993 had been made.

15. Circuit Court, 1996

weight of the panes was within the maximum weights for women in the Manual Handling Regulations 1972, which applied to the plaintiff at the time of her accident in 1992. He also accepted that the training would have alerted the plaintiff to the general dangers involved in manual lifting, though he was of the view that it did not deal with the specific task she was engaged in. He was also of the opinion that there should have been some control on the number of glass panes being lifted by the plaintiff.

The judge dismissed the plaintiff's claim. He accepted that the company had provided a safe system of work and adequate training in manual handling because the training by the physiotherapist had dealt with safe lifting, holding and carrying of objects, and it covered the type of stooping involved in lifting the glass panes in this case. He also noted that the plaintiff had done the same work for over three years without incident; in this time she had assembled about 200 frames a day, coming to a total of about 150,000 frames.

It should be noted that, in these two cases where no liability was imposed – and also in those cases where the employer was found liable – the claim focused on a specific aspect of manual handling. Other issues might arise in different contexts, such as whether sufficient mechanisation has been considered, rather than merely the issue of unsafe procedures or the adequacy of training. In that respect, it is important to note that the Manual Handling Regulations 2007 (in a similar manner to the 1993 Regulations before them) set out a comprehensive set of rules on the topic.

Manual Handling and Human Rights

The connection between manual handling and the European Convention on Human Rights (ECHR) was discussed by the English

High Court in *R. (A and B)* v *East Sussex County Council*.[16] In this case, two sisters A and B, who were profoundly disabled and suffered from learning difficulties, successfully applied (with the support of the British Disability Rights Commission) for a declaration that East Sussex County Council's (ESCC) virtual 'blanket no manual lifting policy' was illegal. The sisters lived with their parents in a house which had been specially adapted. Under British legislation, they were entitled to care from the local authority. As a result of some incidents, A and B and their parents challenged the ESCC's policy of not permitting care staff to lift A and B manually.

The English High Court judge, Mr Justice Munby, held that it was not 'reasonably practicable' for the ESCC to avoid the need for their employees to undertake manual handling of A and B altogether. Justice Munby accepted that the ESCC's revised manual handling policy, which was presented to the Court after the case had begun and which made clear that it did not have a blanket no manual lifting policy, was lawful and 'representative of good practice'. It was therefore compatible with the British Manual Handling Operations Regulations 1992 (which implemented the 1990 EC Manual Handling Directive, 90/269/EEC) and with the ECHR, which had been implemented in the UK by the Human Rights Act 1998.

So the new policy of the ESCC shifted the dispute from being an issue about the lawfulness of the ESCC's alleged blanket no manual lifting policy to being an issue about whether A and B were entitled to be manually lifted by their carers. Justice Munby held that they were. He held that the British 1992 Regulations established a clear hierarchy of safety measures but were a risk reduction/minimisation

---

16. High Court of England and Wales, February 2003

regime and not 'a no risk regime'. There was, he noted, no 'absolute prohibition on hazardous lifting'. Rather, the employer's duty was to avoid or minimise the risk in so far as is reasonably practicable.

In the case of A and B, and when considering the needs of those with a disability, the term reasonably practicable must, he said, take account of the rights of disabled persons in the ECHR. The reasonably practicable test must now, where the disabled are concerned, 'be informed' by the ECHR. An assessment of what is reasonably practicable should consider: (a) the possible methods of avoiding or minimising the risk; (b) the context (frequency and duration of manoeuvres); (c) the risks to employees (likelihood and severity); and (d) the impact on the disabled person. He could not accept the statement of an expert witness 'that manual lifting is permissible only if the lift cannot be carried out using a hoist (that is, physically impossible)' or 'in exceptional circumstances', such as 'a prolonged power failure, fire or other life threatening occurrence'.

While this decision might not be followed exactly in Ireland, it is worth noting that Irish courts are also required to take account of the ECHR because it too has been implemented in Ireland by the European Convention on Human Rights Act 2003, which is modelled on the UK Human Rights Act 1998.[17]

---

17. The European Convention on Human Rights Act 2003 was enacted as part of a series of legislative and other measures arising from the 1998 Belfast Agreements (also known as the Good Friday Agreements).

Web Resources

Health and Safety Authority, *Caring with Minimal Lifting* (2007), available online at: http://www.hsa.ie/eng/Publications_and_ Forms/Publications/Occupational_Health/Caring_with_Minimal _Lifting.pdf

Health and Safety Authority, *Ergonomics in the Workplace*, available online at: http://www.hsa.ie/eng/Publications_and_Forms/ Publications/Occupational_Health/Ergonomics.pdf

Health and Safety Authority, *Guidance on the Management of Manual Handling in the Workplace* (2005), available online at: http://www.hsa.ie/eng/Publications_and_Forms/Publications/ Occupational_Health/Guidance_on_the_Management_of_ Manual_Handling_in_the_Workplace.html

Health and Safety Authority, *Guide on Manual Handling Risk Assessment in the Hospitality Sector*, available online at: http:// www.hsa.ie/eng/Publications_and_Forms/Publications/Retail/ Hospitality_Sector.pdf

Health and Safety Authority, *Guide on Manual Handling Risk Assessment in the Retail Sector* (2010), available online at: http://www.hsa.ie/eng/Publications_and_Forms/Publications/ Occupational_Health/Guide_on_Manual_Handling_Risk_ Assessment_in_the_Retail_Sector.html

Health and Safety Authority, *Guide to Manual Handling Training System – 2010 Revision* (2010), available online at: http://www.

hsa.ie/eng/Publications_and_Forms/Publications/Occupational_ Health/Guidance_on_the_Manual_Handling_Training_ System_-_2010_revision.html

Health and Safety Authority, *Guide to the Safety, Health and Welfare at Work (General Application) Regulations 2007: Chapter 4 of Part 2: Manual Handling of Loads* (2007), available online at: http:// www.hsa.ie/eng/Publications_and_Forms/Publications/Retail/ Gen_Apps_Manual_Handling.pdf

Office of the Attorney General, Safety, Health and Welfare at Work Act 2005, available online at: www.irishstatute.ie

Office of the Attorney General, SI No. 299/2007 – Safety, Health and Welfare at Work (General Application) Regulations 2007, available online at: www.irishstatute.ie